Heinkel He 111

in action

By George Punka

Color by Don Greer

Illustrated by John Lowe

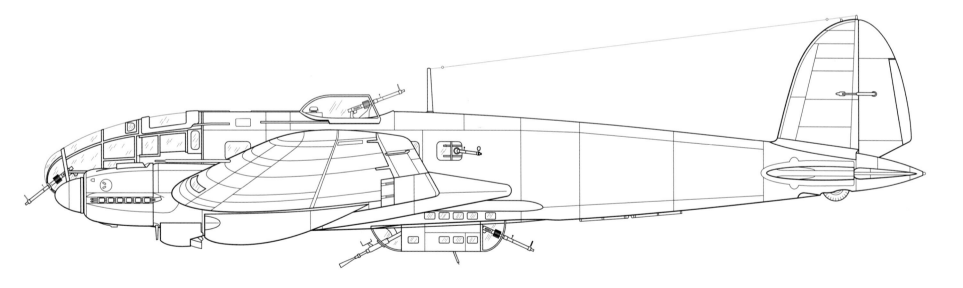

Aircraft Number 184

squadron/signal publications

An He 111H-3 (1H+AS) leads several other aircraft of III *Gruppe* (Group), *Kampfgeschwader* (KG; Bomber Wing) 26 *'Löwengeschwader'* across the English coast near Newcastle on 15 September 1940. The 'Lions Wing' bombers were based at Stavanger-Sola airfield in Norway during the Battle of Britain. British fighters shot down eight of the 72 He 111s launched on this raid.

Acknowledgements

Pál Bagossy	Josef Schmidt
Jules Bernard	Hans Gottfried Schulz
Hans Höhler	Hans-Heiri Stapfer
Dr. Volker Koos	War's End
Ferenc Kovács	László Winkler
Franz Löhr	Zsák Archiv
Imre Mészáros	*Etablissement Cinématographique et*
Peter Mujzer	*Photographique des Armées* (ECPA)
Peter Petrick	Bundesarchiv
Punka Archiv	Michael Schmeelke

Dedication:

For 'Dorka' Péterdy

ISBN 0-89747-446-5

If you have any photographs of aircraft, armor, soldiers or ships of any nation, particularly wartime snapshots, why not share them with us and help make Squadron/Signal's books all the more interesting and complete in the future. Any photograph sent to us will be copied and the original returned. The donor will be fully credited for any photos used. Please send them to:

Squadron/Signal Publications, Inc.
1115 Crowley Drive
Carrollton, TX 75011-5010

Если у вас есть фотографии самолётов, вооружения, солдат или кораблей любой страны, особенно, снимки времён войны, поделитесь с нами и помогите сделать новые книги издательства Эскадрон/Сигнал ещё интереснее. Мы переснимем ваши фотографии и вернём оригиналы. Имена приславших снимки будут сопровождать все опубликованные фотографии. Пожалуйста, присылайте фотографии по адресу:

Squadron/Signal Publications, Inc.
1115 Crowley Drive
Carrollton, TX 75011-5010

軍用機、装甲車両、兵士、軍艦などの写真を所持しておられる方はいらっしゃいませんか？どの国のものでも結構です。作戦中に撮影されたものが特に良いのです。Squadron/Signal社の出版する刊行物において、このような写真は内容を一層充実し、興味深くすることができます。当方にお送り頂いた写真は、複写の後お返しいたします。出版物中に写真を使用した場合は、必ず提供者のお名前を明記させて頂きます。お写真は下記にご送付ください。

Squadron/Signal Publications, Inc.
1115 Crowley Drive
Carrollton, TX 75011-5010

A formation of He 111H-16s heads for their target over the Eastern Front in the summer of 1941. These aircraft were assigned to *Kampfgeschwader* (KG; Bomber Wing) 53. Undersurface wingtips and aft fuselage bands are RLM 27 Yellow (FS33637) for Axis aircraft operating on this front during World War Two. The near aircraft has the *Staffel* (Squadron) code letter J immediately aft of the fuselage *Balkenkreuz* (Beam Cross) national insignia. (Bundesarchiv)

Introduction

In early 1932, the German airline *Deutsche Lufthansa* (DLH) sought a high-speed, small-capacity airliner for its domestic routes. The Ernst Heinkel AG (*Aktiengesellschaft*; Joint-Stock Company) responded to this requirement with the He 70 *Blitz* (Lightning), which first flew on 1 December 1932. This single-engine, all-metal monoplane with retracting undercarriage impressed DLH with its performance. Heinkel delivered 12 production He 70s to DLH, which placed the aircraft into commercial service on 15 June 1934.

After the He 70's successful entry into service, DLH decided to expand their air routes. It asked Heinkel to develop a new high-speed airliner, which accommodated ten passengers and a crew of two. Although most of the designers of the time would have chosen a three-engine aircraft for safety reasons, the Heinkel team put aerodynamic characteristics first and chose a twin-engine design for the **He 111**.

Design work on the He 111 began in early 1934, led by engineers Siegfried Günter and Karl Schwärzler. The He 111 followed the basic lines of the He 70 and was an all-metal, flush-riveted, streamlined aircraft with elliptical wings and stabilizers, a retractable main undercarriage, and a fixed tail skid. It had a long, slender nose with a clear cone for the bombardier. After numerous evaluations and wind-tunnel tests, a full-scale mockup was built in 1934. The newly formed *Reichsluftfahrtministerium* (RLM; Reich Air Ministry) was impressed with this design and requested Heinkel to develop a medium level bomber version of this aircraft.

The first prototype was the **He 111a** (D-ADAP, *Werk Nr.*[1] 713-V1), which was completed at Heinkel's Marienehe plant near Rostock. It made several taxi tests before making its first flight from the Rostock-Marienehe airfield on 24 February 1935, with Heinkel chief test pilot Gerhard Nitschke at the controls. He was highly satisfied with this flight, particularly praising the He 111a's flying, handling, and outstanding landing characteristics. Nitschke found the new aircraft's longitudinal stability unsatisfactory during the second test flight a few days later. He recommended several modifications, including increasing the horizontal stabilizers, improving the elevator alignment, rearranging the throttle position in the cockpit, and glazing the entire nose section. The modifications were made and the aircraft was flown to the RLM's *E-Stelle*[2] at Rechlin for further tests.

The He 111a (later redesignated the **He 111 V1**[3]) had a wingspan of 25 M (82 feet 0.3 inches), a length of 17.38 M (57 feet 0.3 inches), and a height of 4.1 M (13 feet 5.4 inches). The elliptical wing's area amounted to 87.6 M^2 (942.9 square feet). The He 111a weighed 5782 KG (12,746.9 pounds) empty and 7590 KG (16,732.8 pounds) fully loaded.

This aircraft was powered by two 660 HP BMW VI.6.0 Z 12-cylinder, liquid-cooled, inline engines. These engines powered the He 111a to a maximum speed of 349 KMH (216.9 MPH) at 5400 M (17,716.5 feet). It had a service ceiling of 6000 M (19,685 feet) and a maximum range of 1500 KM (932.1 miles).

Heinkel built two additional prototypes in parallel to the He 111a. The **He 111c** (D-ALIX, *Werk Nr.* 715) first flew on 12 March 1935 – 16 days after the He 111a's maiden flight. This aircraft was similar to the earlier He 111a, but featured a different wing. Although the trailing edge had a reduced curvature and the wingspan was reduced to 23 M (75 feet 5.5 inches), the wing area was increased to 88.5 M^2 (952.6 square feet). The He 111c was later designated **He 111 V3** and was the first prototype of a commercial version of this aircraft. Power was supplied by two 750 HP BMW VI U vee engines, which turned two-bladed adjustable pitch pro-

[1] *Werk Nr.: Werk Nummer* (Factory Number), which the Germans used as the aircraft's serial number.

[2] *E-Stelle: Erprobungsstelle*, Test Center

[3] V: *Versuch*, Experimental

The Heinkel He 70 light transport first flew in late 1932. Its all-metal structure included elliptical wings and tail surfaces and fully retractable main landing gear. These features were incorporated into the later and larger He 111 bomber. This He 70F-1 was assigned to 3 *Staffel* of *Aufklärungsgruppe* (Reconnaissance Group) (F)/123 in 1936.

The Heinkel He 111c (later He 111 V3) airliner was built parallel with the first He 111 prototype (He 111a, later He 111 V1), which was configured as a bomber. The second aircraft was rolled out from Heinkel's factory 16 days after the He 111a's maiden flight. This aircraft (D-ALIX) was named ROSTOCK by *Deutsche Lufthansa* (DLH). (Winkler)

pellers. DLH named it ROSTOCK when it was accepted in late 1935 and the He 111 V3 was used for mail service to South America during the mid to late 1930s.

The **He 111b** (D-ALES) second bomber prototype soon followed the He 111c. It was identical to the two previous He 111s, except for the wing. The He 111b's wing was similar to that of the He 111c, but with more sharply curved tips for a reduced span of 22.6 M (74 feet 1.8 inches) and a similar wing area to that of the He 111a. Its gross weight was increased to 7700 KG (16,975.3 pounds). The He 111b was designated **He 111 V2** in late 1935.

This prototype led to the pre-production **He 111A-0** medium-bomber in early 1936. The ten aircraft built had an extended nose with extensive glazing for the navigator/bombardier. This increased the He 111A's length from 17.38 M to 17.5 M (57 feet 5 inches). The aircraft had a maximum bomb load of 1000 KG (2204.6 pounds). The He 111A-0 was armed with three 7.92MM Rheinmetall MG 15[4] machine guns: one each in the nose (*A-Stand*[5]), the open dorsal position (*B-Stand*), and the retractable ventral 'dustbin' position (*C-Stand*). The 'dustbin' caused drag on the aircraft when it was lowered. Its four-man crew consisted of pilot, navigator/bombardier, radio operator/dorsal gunner, and ventral gunner.

During the first military trials, the He 111A-0 achieved a maximum speed of 310 KMH (192.6 MPH) and a ceiling of 5500 M (18,044.6 feet). This was achieved with an 8700 KG (19,179.9 pound) take-off weight and the 'dustbin' lowered. Its had a range of 1100 KM (683.5 miles) with a 1000 KG (2204.6 pound) load. The cruising speed ranged between 250 and 275 KMH (155.3-170.9 MPH). The He 111A-0 weighed 999.7 KG (2203.9 pounds) greater than the He 111 V2, with no change in the powerplant. This resulted in the pre-production aircraft being underpowered and led the Luftwaffe to reject the He 111A-0 for service. Germany sold all ten aircraft built to China in 1936. It is believed these He 111As saw combat against invading Japanese forces during the Sino-Japanese War, which began on 7 July 1937.

In the meantime, Heinkel built two additional He 111 prototypes in late 1935. The **He 111d** (later **He 111 V4**) was the second commercial prototype, which flew in late 1935. It was assigned the civil registration D-AHAO and later named DRESDEN. The He 111 V4 had a similar wing to the He 111 V1 and was powered by two 660 HP BMW VI 6.OZ engines turning three-bladed variable pitch propellers. Heinkel used the He 111 V4 for flight testing until delivering it to DLH, which used it for route proving flights until 1937.

The **He 111e** (later **He 111 V5**, D-APYS) was the third bomber prototype and made its maiden flight during the early winter of 1936. It used the He 111A-0 airframe, with the fuselage length at 17.5 M (57 feet 5 inches), while the wingspan was reduced from 25 M to 22.61 M (74 feet 2.2 inches). It weighed 5400 KG (11,904.8 pounds) empty and 8209 KG (18,097.4 pounds) fully loaded.

Provision was made for three 7.92MM MG 15 machine guns in the nose, dorsal, and ventral positions. The He 111 V5 had an interior bomb bay for a 1000 KG (2204.6 pound) bomb load, with the bombs carried vertically (nose-up) in eight cells. This aircraft was originally equipped with 660 HP BMW VI 6.0Z engines, which were insufficient for the aircraft. Its maximum speed was reduced to 308 KMH (191.4 MPH), compared to the He 111 V1's 349 KMH (216.9 MPH) top speed. The He 111 V5 was retrofitted with two 950 HP Daimler-Benz DB 600A 12-cylinder, liquid-cooled, inline engines. Oil cooling problems were soon discovered, due to using the smaller coolers fitted with the BMW engines. Heinkel engineers enlarged these oil coolers and placed them under the wings and flanking the engine nacelles. This solved the cooling problem and allowed the He 111 V5 to achieve its designed performance. The Luftwaffe was impressed by this aircraft and ordered it into production as the **He 111B** in 1936.

---

[4]MG: *Maschinengewehr*, Machine Gun

[5]*Stand*, Position

The He 111 V4 (D-AHAO, DRESDEN) was demonstrated to the press for the first time at Berlin's Tempelhof airport on 10 January 1936. This aircraft was the second commercial prototype and featured the slightly longer wings of the earlier He 111 V1. Two 660 HP BMW VI 6.0 Z 12-cylinder inline engines powered the V4. (Winkler)

The He 111A-0 was the initial pre-production variant, which was introduced in early 1936. This aircraft (*Werk Nummer*/Factory Number 1438) was one of ten A-0s built. This variant had an extended and more extensively glazed nose than the He 111b (He 111 V2) on which it was based. (Punka Archiv)

Development

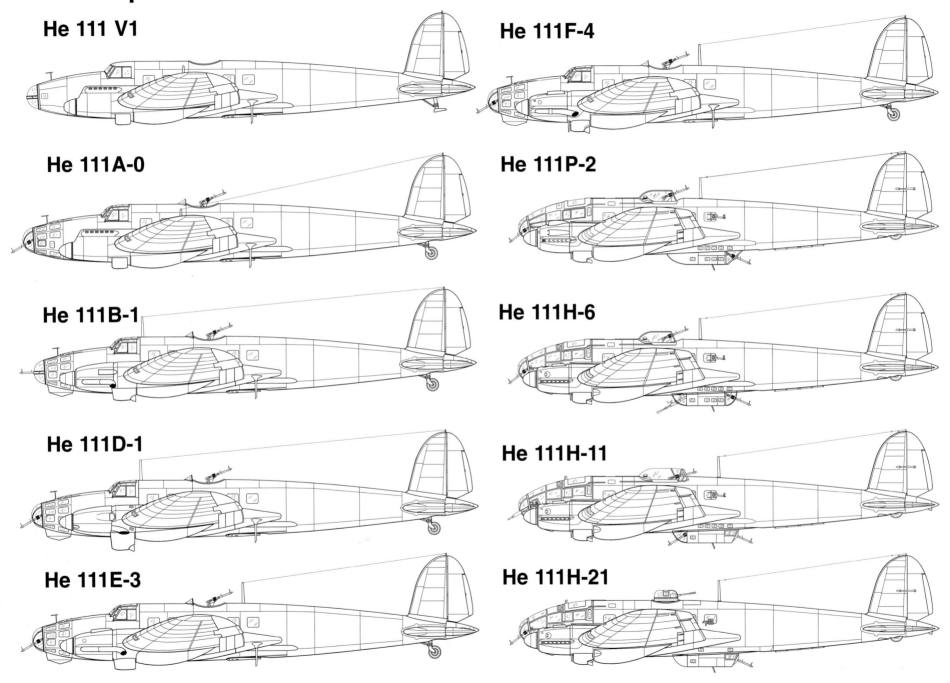

He 111 V1

He 111A-0

He 111B-1

He 111D-1

He 111E-3

He 111F-4

He 111P-2

He 111H-6

He 111H-11

He 111H-21

He 111B

The first pre-production **He 111B-0**s (*Werk Nr.* 1431) made its maiden flight from Rostock-Marienehe in March of 1936. This and six subsequent aircraft were powered by two 950 HP Daimler-Benz DB 600C 12-cylinder, liquid-cooled, inline engines. The bombers were later retrofitted with 1050 HP DB 600Ga engines. Serial production began at Rostock in the summer of 1936 and the first examples were delivered to the *E-Stelle* (Test Center) at Rechlin in the fall of 1936. The fourth He 111B-0 (*Werk Nr.* 1434, D-ARAU) was equipped with external bomb racks for trial purposes; however, it crashed at Rechlin on 24 March 1937. The seventh He 111B-0 (*Werk Nr.* 1437) was used for flight trials of the 1100 HP DB 601 engines.

The He 111B-0 was armed with three 7.92MM Rheinmetall MG 15 machine guns. One weapon each was mounted in the nose cone (*A-Stand*), the open dorsal position (*B-Stand*), and in a retractable ventral 'dustbin' position (*C-Stand*). The 'dustbin' caused major drag when it was lowered, reducing its maximum speed to 309 KMH (192 MPH). This was only done when enemy fighter attacks were imminent. The bomb bay held a maximum load of 1500 KG (3306.9 pounds), in eight vertical cells arranged in two rows of four cells per row.

The He 111B-0 retained the same external dimensions as the earlier He 111A-0 bombers. The new aircraft had a wingspan of 22.6 M (74 feet 1.8 inches), with a length of 17.5 M (57 feet 5 inches) and a height of 4.2 M (13 feet 9.4 inches). It weighed 5800 KG (12,786.6 pounds) empty and 8600 KG (18,959.4 pounds) fully loaded. The He 111B-0 had a maximum speed of 370 KMH (229.9 MPH) at 4000 M (13,123.4 feet) and a cruising speed of 340 KMH (211.3 MPH). It had a service ceiling of 7000 M (22,965.9 feet) and a range of 1065 KM (661.8 miles). Tanks inside the wings held 2425 L (640.6 gallons) of 87 octane B4 grade fuel. The He 111B-0 had a crew of four: pilot, navigator/bombardier, radio operator/dorsal gunner, and ventral gunner.

Service tests at Rechlin revealed few problems with this aircraft. Changes included repositioning some service equipment items (including radios and navigation equipment) and correcting a minor aileron fault, which affected handling at certain speeds. The Luftwaffe approved Heinkel's aircraft for service and authorized production of 50 **He 111B-1** bombers in late 1936. A factory allocated to He 111 production was established at Oranienburg, north-west of Berlin. This joined Heinkel's Rostock-Marienehe plant in producing this bomber. Licensed production also began at the Norddeutschen Dornier-Werke in Wismar, ATG in Leipzig, and Arado Brandenburg in Havel. The first He 111-equipped *Kampfgeschwader* (KG; Bomber Wing) was KG 154 *'Boelcke'* (later redesignated KG 27). This unit was based at Hannover-Langenhagen and received its first He 111B-1s in early 1937. Early He 111B-1s were powered by 950 HP DB 600A series engines, while later aircraft had the 850 HP DB 600C series engines.

In May of 1937, production at Oranienburg switched to the **He 111B-2**. Other factories ended He 111B-1 production in favor of this new variant in early June. The He 111B-2 was identical to the He 111B-1, but was powered by 950 HP DB 600CG engines. The powerplants featured individual exhaust pipes, which replaced the B-1's clustered exhausts. Auxiliary radiators were mounted on the wing leading edges, flanking the engine nacelles. These provided additional cooling for the DB 600CG engines. The B-2's nose was modified to have fewer frames, which improved the navigator/bombardier's visibility. The nose machine gun mount was replaced by an Ikaria GD-A 1114 ball-type mounting, which provided a greater field of fire.

The He 111B-2 had a maximum speed of 370 KMH (229.9 MPH) at 4000 M. The new variant's cruising speed improved from 365 KMH (226.8 MPH) for late B-1s to 369 KMH (229.3 MPH). All other specifications and armament remained the same as for the He 111B-1.

The five factories in Germany built approximately 300 He 111Bs through early 1938. The Germans deployed several He 111B-1/B-2 aircraft to Spain during that country's civil war in early 1937. These bombers served with two *Staffeln* (Squadrons) of *Kampfgruppe* (Bomber Group) 88, the bombing element of the *Legion Condor*. This Legion was Germany's principal contribution to the Spanish Nationalist war effort.

After the Spanish Civil War ended in March of 1939, the Luftwaffe relegated the He 111B series to training purposes. This was due to new and improved He 111 variants entering service during this period. The Weser-Flugzeugbau modified 210 surviving He 111Bs into dual-control trainers for bomber crews by November of 1941.

Two He 111B-2s fly over Germany during a routine training mission. The B-2 replaced the He 111B-1's clustered exhausts with individual exhaust stacks. Auxiliary radiators were fitted to the leading edges of the He 111H-2's wings, near the engine nacelles. Prior to late 1938, the German flag – a black swastika on a white circle in a red field – was painted across the vertical tail surfaces. (Michael Schmeelke)

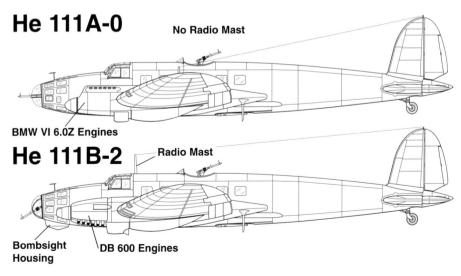

He 111A-0

No Radio Mast

BMW VI 6.0Z Engines

He 111B-2

Radio Mast

Bombsight Housing

DB 600 Engines

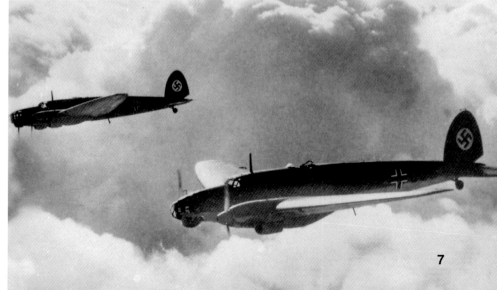

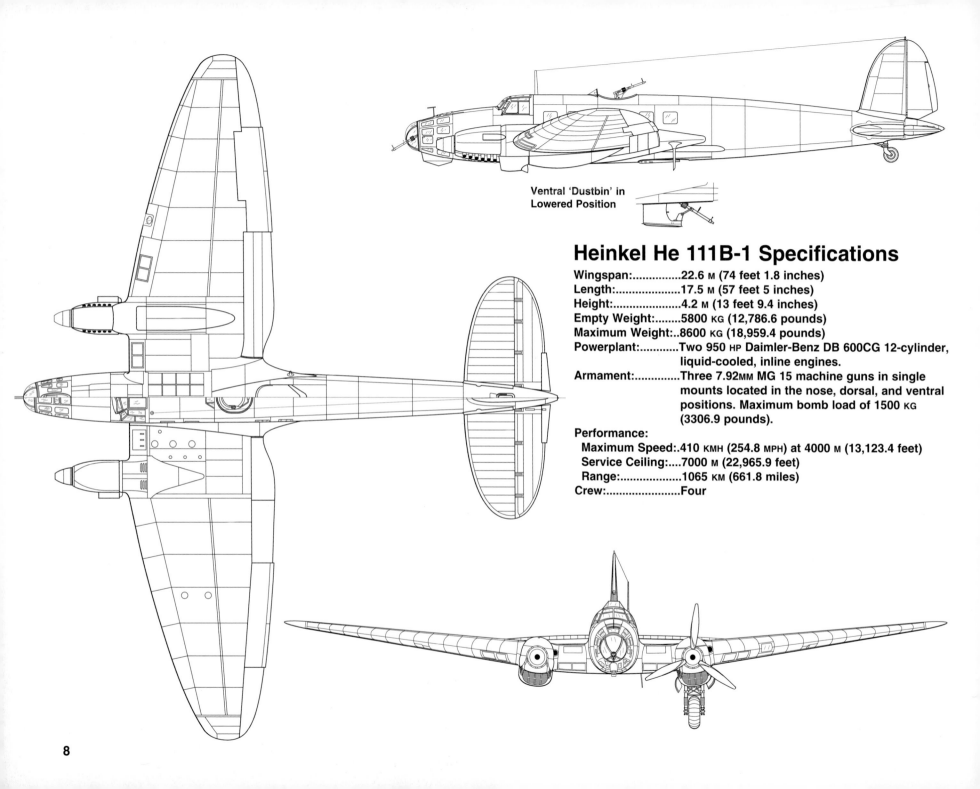

Ventral 'Dustbin' in Lowered Position

Heinkel He 111B-1 Specifications

Wingspan:...............22.6 M (74 feet 1.8 inches)
Length:....................17.5 M (57 feet 5 inches)
Height:....................4.2 M (13 feet 9.4 inches)
Empty Weight:........5800 KG (12,786.6 pounds)
Maximum Weight:..8600 KG (18,959.4 pounds)
Powerplant:............Two 950 HP Daimler-Benz DB 600CG 12-cylinder, liquid-cooled, inline engines.
Armament:..............Three 7.92MM MG 15 machine guns in single mounts located in the nose, dorsal, and ventral positions. Maximum bomb load of 1500 KG (3306.9 pounds).

Performance:
  Maximum Speed:.410 KMH (254.8 MPH) at 4000 M (13,123.4 feet)
  Service Ceiling:....7000 M (22,965.9 feet)
  Range:...................1065 KM (661.8 miles)
Crew:.......................Four

Several crewmen stand under the port nacelle of an He 111B-2, which had landed at Pápa airfield in Hungary on a pre-war training flight. The aircraft was assigned to *Kampfgeschwader* (KG; Bomber Wing) 154 *'Boelcke,'* which was later redesignated KG 27. The Wing was based at Hannover-Langenhagen prior to World War Two. Many early He 111s were modified for Luftwaffe pilot training use during the early war years. (Zsák Archiv)

Nose and Cowling Development

He 111B-1

Early Clear Nose Cone Framing

Short Carburetor Intake

Individual Engine Exhausts

Standard Radiator

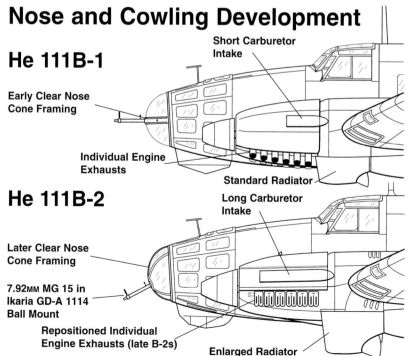

He 111B-2

Later Clear Nose Cone Framing

Long Carburetor Intake

7.92MM MG 15 in Ikaria GD-A 1114 Ball Mount

Repositioned Individual Engine Exhausts (late B-2s)

Enlarged Radiator

The He 111B-2's defensive armament included one 7.92MM Rheinmetall MG 15 machine gun in an Ikaria GD-A 1114 ball-type nose mount. The 75-round ammunition drum was not fitted to this weapon. The navigator/bombardier/nose gunner has opened the port window immediately aft of the nose blister. This allowed for greater ventilation for him and the pilot seated further aft. (Punka Archiv)

Crewmen pose around a map held by a comrade while standing near an He 111B. The flight crews are wearing cold-weather flight clothing. The bomb sight was fitted within the bulge located on the lower nose. An unidentified *Geschwader* (Wing) insignia is painted on the nose.

An He 111B-1 (25-2) is parked on a Spanish airfield in late 1936 or early 1937. A tarpaulin was placed over the dorsal gunner's position. The Spanish Nationalists assigned the code number 25 to He 111s, while this was the second He 111 in Nationalist service. PEDRO – the Spanish nickname for the He 111 – is white on the nose. He 111Bs were assigned to a pair of squadrons in K/88 (*Kampfgruppe*; Bomber Group), *Legion Condor*. (Punka Archiv)

An He 111B-1 (V4+EH) of KG 1 *'Hindenburg'* flies along the Baltic coast in 1939. This variant was equipped with 950 HP Daimler-Benz DB 600CG engines. KG 1 attacked Polish fleet installations on the first morning of the Second World War, 1 September 1939. The Wing's insignia used the coat of arms of World War One hero Field Marshal Paul von Hindenburg (Löhr)

Ventral 'Dustbin' Gunner's Position, Extended

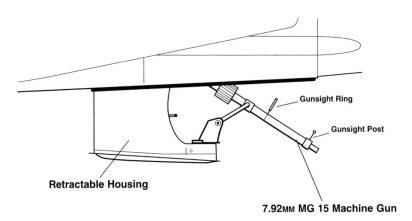

Gunsight Ring

Gunsight Post

Retractable Housing

7.92MM MG 15 Machine Gun

He 111C and He 111G

Further development of the He 111 V2 (formerly He 111c) airliner prototype culminated in the He 111 V-4 (D-AHAO), the definitive configuration for the *Deutsche Lufthansa* (DLH) aircraft. DLH designated this aircraft as the **He 111C-0**, which was flown by two crew members and carried ten passengers.

The new airliner was presented to the press at Berlin-Tempelhof airport on 10 January 1936. Six He 111C-0s were built, each powered by two 750 HP BMW VI U inline engines. DLH declined to purchase more aircraft because their lack of engine power made the operating cost too high. Nevertheless, the six He 111C-0s entered scheduled service in the summer of 1937.

In 1937, one He 111C and two prototypes (He 111 V2 and V4) were delivered to *Kommando Rowehl*. This was a top secret Luftwaffe unit established under the command of *Oberstleutnant* (Lt Col) Theodor Rowehl and based at Staaken, just west of Berlin. The unit carried out secret long-range photo reconnaissance missions over the Soviet Union, France, and Great Britain, which were disguised as commercial route-proving flights.

Heinkel tried once more to break into the commercial aviation field with the **He 111G** in 1937. This aircraft was based on the He 111 V-4 prototype and featured a new straight-tapered wing, which was easier to produce than the He 111C's elliptical wing. The **He 111G-01** (**He 111 V12**, D-AEQA) and the **He 111G-02** (**He 111 V13**, D-AYKI) were built and tested in 1937. Each aircraft was powered by two 660 HP BMW VI 6.0 ZU 12-cylinder, liquid-cooled, inline engines. In 1938, these aircraft were delivered to DLH and named HALLE and MAGDEBURG, respectively.

Two **He 111G-3** series aircraft were built with BMW nine-cylinder, air-cooled, radial engines. The **He 111 V14** (D-ACBS, AUGSBURG, *Werk Nr.* 1884) had 850 HP BMW 132Dc powerplants, while the **He 111 V15** (D-ACDF, DRESDEN, *Werk Nr.* 1885) had 1000 HP BMW 132H engines. These aircraft were transferred from the RLM to DLH – which redesignated them as **He 111L**s – in 1938.

The **He 111 V16** (D-ASAR, *Werk Nr.* 2469) was the first of five **He 111G-4**s built (*Werk Nr.* 2469-2473). This aircraft was powered by two 900 HP Daimler-Benz DB 600G 12-cylinder, liquid-cooled, inline engines. The first He 111G-4 later served as the personal aircraft of *Generalfeldmarschall* (Field Marshal) Erhard Milch, the Luftwaffe's deputy commander-in-chief. The four **He 111G-5**s built (*Werk Nr.* 5067-5070) were similar to the He 111G-4, but were powered by two 950 HP DB 600Ga engines. All four examples were sold to Turkey in 1938.

Most DLH He 111C/Gs were impressed into the Luftwaffe after World War Two began on 1 September 1939. These airliners were converted into air force liaison aircraft early in the conflict and served for much of the war.

(Right) This He 111G-5 (PF+UP) has delivered a German military delegation to Budaörs airfield in Hungary sometime between 1941 and 1944. The port 7.92MM MG 15 machine gun was removed from the aft window. The He 111G-5 is camouflaged in RLM 70 Black Green (FS34050) and RLM 71 Dark Green (FS34079) upper surfaces, with an RLM 27 Yellow (FS33637) aft fuselage band. Fuselage codes were RLM 22 Black (FS37038), while the undersurfaces were RLM 65 Light Blue (FS35352). (Punka Archiv)

(Above) D-AQYF LEIPZIG was one of six He 111C-0 pre-production airliners completed in the summer of 1936. This ten-passenger aircraft began operating scheduled services with Deutsche Lufthansa (DLH) during the summer of 1937. DLH He 111Cs were left in natural metal, with black markings and trim and the Nazi flag on the vertical tail. Most DLH He 111s were impressed into the Luftwaffe when World War Two began. (Winkler)

An He 111D-1 assigned the civil registration D-ADCU is parked at a German airfield in 1937. This variant was powered by two 865 HP DB 600Aa engines and armed with three 7.92MM MG 15 machine guns. The pre-1939 Luftwaffe camouflage scheme had upper sur-faces in RLM 61 Dark Brown (FS30040), RLM 62 Green (FS34128), and RLM 63 Green Gray (FS36373). The Nazi flag on the tail consisted of a black *Hakenkreuz* (swastika) in a white disc on a red field. (Punka Archiv)

Another He 111D-1 rests between missions in late 1938 or early 1939. The MG 15s were mounted in the nose, dorsal, and ventral 'dustbin' positions, which were the same for early He 111s. Undersurfaces on Luftwaffe aircraft were RLM 65 Light Blue (FS35352) at the time. The red tail band and much of the white disc were overpainted with RLM 62 Green in late 1938 to reduce their visibility. The black letters OHA under the wing formed part of this aircraft's civil registration, which is believed to be D-AOHA.

He 111D

In 1937, Heinkel modified an He 111B-0 by installing two 950 HP Daimler-Benz DB 600Ga inline engines. This variant replaced the He 111B-2's supplemental radiators under the wing leading edges with a larger radiator mounted under the engine. The aircraft was redesignated the **He 111 V9**, assigned the civil registration D-AQOX, and began flight trials in the summer of 1937. The He 111 V9 served as the prototype for the **He 111D** series, which began with the **He 111D-0** pre-production aircraft. Its wingspan was 22.6 M (74 feet 1.8 inches), with a length of 17.5 M (57 feet 5 inches), and a height of 4.2 M (13 feet 9.4 inches). Its empty weight increased from the He 111B-2's 5800 KG (12,786.6 pounds) to 6000 KG (13,227.5 pounds), while take-off weight went from 8600 KG (18,959.4 pounds) to 8800 KG (19,400.4 pounds). Despite this weight increase, the He 111D-0's maximum speed improved from 370 KMH (229.9 MPH) to 410 KMH (254.8 MPH) at 4000 M (13,123.4 feet). Other performance data were nearly identical to the He 111B-2.

Heinkel built at least three He 111D-0s before completing ten **He 111D-1** and ten **He 111D-2** aircraft by May of 1939. These production aircraft were equipped with additional radio equipment for use as flying regimental level command stations. Two radio operators, a navigational officer, and a spare crew member were added to the standard He 111 flight crew (pilot, navigator/bombardier, radio operator/dorsal gunner, and ventral gunner). The He 111D-1 and He 111D-2 differed only in the radio equipment fitted. The He 111D-1 had two FuG IIIa U1 units built into its bomb bay, while the D-2 replaced these with a larger FuG IIIa Y set. He 111Ds were armed with one 7.92MM MG 15 machine gun in each of the nose (*A-Stand*), dorsal (*B-Stand*), and ventral (*C-Stand*) 'dustbin' positions.

He 111D production ended in late 1937, due to heavy demand for their DB 600 engines. This powerplant was also used by the Messerschmitt Bf 109 and Bf 110 fighters. None of the approximately 23 He 111Ds built were assigned to Luftwaffe *Kampfgeschwadern* (Bomber Wings), but were employed on test duties.

[1]FuG: *Funk Gerät*, Radio Set

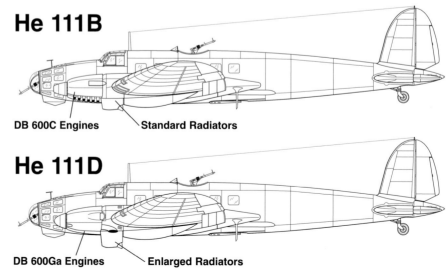

He 111B

DB 600C Engines   Standard Radiators

He 111D

DB 600Ga Engines   Enlarged Radiators

He 111E

An He 111B-0 was fitted with two 730 HP Junkers Jumo 210Ga 12-cylinder, liquid-cooled, inline engines in 1937. This aircraft was redesignated the **He 111 V6** (D-AXOH) and used for flight tests, which soon highlighted the powerplant's shortcomings. The He 111 V6 was reengined with the 1000 HP Jumo 211A-1 and later transferred to Junkers for propeller testing.

Heinkel then converted an He 111D-0 into the **He 111 V10** (D-ALEQ), which also had Jumo 211A-1 engines. Semi-retractable engine radiators were fitted for improved engine cooling. This aircraft served as the prototype for the **He 111E** series aircraft, but was later destroyed by an engine fire during experimental radiator testing.

The first two pre-production **He 111E-0**s – He 111D-1s refitted with the new engines and radiators – were completed in January of 1938. This variant's bomb load increased from the He 111B's 1500 KG (3306.9 pounds) to 1700 KG (3747.8 pounds). These weapons were loaded vertically (nose up) in the eight bomb bay compartments, which restricted the maximum bomb size to 250 KG (551.1 pounds). The He 111E-0's maximum weight also went up to 10,297 KG (22,700.6 pounds), compared to the D's 8800 KG (19,400.4 pounds). The external dimensions remained unchanged: wingspan of 22.6 M (74 feet 1.8 inches), length of 17.5 M (57 feet 5 inches), and height of 4.2 M (13 feet 9.4 inches). The radio antenna mast was moved from just aft of the cockpit to the mid-fuselage, aft of the dorsal gunner's position.

The initial production variant was the **He 111E-1**, which first appeared in February of 1938. This version had a further increase in bomb load over the He 111E-0, to 2000 KG (4409.2 pounds). The He 111E-1's maximum take off weight increased to 10,600 KG (23,368.6 pounds). German factories built approximately 120 He 111E-1s and one **He 111E-2**, which had minor equipment changes. In March of 1938, the Germans deployed 45 He 111E-1s to Spain for service with the *Legion Condor* during the Spanish Civil War. After the conflict ended in early 1939, the Germans turned over several He 111E-1s to the Spanish Air Force.[1]

The next major E series variant was the **He 111E-3**, which followed in February of 1938. Heinkel built 67 He 111E-3s, with the last 44 aircraft having increased fuel capacity. Two outboard wing tanks with a total capacity of 1025 L (270.8 gallons) were installed on the latter aircraft. This increased the He 111E-3's total fuel capacity from 2425 L (640.6 gallons) to 3450 L (911.4 gallons).

[1]Spanish Air Force; in Spanish, *Ejército del Aire Español.*

The He 111E-3 had a wingspan of 22.6 M (74 feet 1.8 inches), a length of 17.5 M (57 feet 5 inches), and a height of 4.2 m (13 feet 9.4 inches). Its empty weight was 6140 KG (13,536.2 pounds), while its maximum take off weight amounted to 10,500 KG (23,148.1 pounds). The He 111E-3 had a maximum speed of 420 KMH (261 MPH) at 5000 M (16,404.2 feet), while its cruising speed was 380 KMH (236.1 MPH). It had a service ceiling of 8000 M (26,246.7 feet) and a range of 1065 KM (661.8 miles).

Defensive armament for the He 111E-3 consisted of three 7.92MM Rheinmetall MG 15 machine guns. These were fitted into single mounts located in the nose cone, open dorsal, and ventral 'dustbin' positions. It carried a 2000 KG (4409.2 pound) bomb load in eight bomb bay compartments. The He 111E-3 was crewed by four men: pilot, navigator/bombardier, radio operator/dorsal gunner, and ventral gunner.

Approximately ten **He 111E-4** bombers were built in 1938. These aircraft replaced the earlier variants' eight bomb bay compartments with two external bomb racks on the centerline. Each rack could hold up to 1000 KG (2204.6 pounds) of ordnance. The approximately ten **He 111E-5**s built were similar to He 111E-4s, but added a 835 L (220.6 gallon) auxiliary fuel tank to the port bomb bay area. This increased the fuel capacity to 4285 L (1132 gallons), but reduced the internal bomb load to 1000 KG.

The Luftwaffe ordered 294 He 111Es; however, changing service requirements reduced this to 210 aircraft. These and other early He 111s were built at Heinkel's Marienehe and Oranienburg plants. Additional license production was performed at Norddeutschen Dornier-Werke/Wismar, Arado Brandenburg/Havel, and ATG/Leipzig.

The Germans converted several He 111E-3s into dual-control training machines for service early in World War Two. Thirty surviving He 111Es were equipped for Luftwaffe target-towing duties in 1940. Several He 111Es in Spain served as bombers until the mid-1940s, when they were relegated to the transport and training roles. These He 111Es remained in Spanish Air Force service until the late 1950s.

This He 111E-4 (CH+NR) was converted from a bomber to a transport early in World War Two. Passenger seating was added inside the fuselage and the external bomb racks were removed. The retractable 'dustbin' was removed and replaced by a ventral fairing. He 111E-4s were powered by 1000 HP Junkers Jumo 211A-1 inline engines. (Löhr)

He 111D

DB 600 Ga Engines

Large Radiators

He 111E

Repositioned Antenna Mast

Jumo 211A-1 Engines

Smaller Radiators

(Above) An He 111E is parked at a Luftwaffe base in France following the 1940 German campaign in Western Europe. This aircraft was used as a transport, with defensive armament and bomb racks deleted. Jumo 211 engines fitted to He 111Es had exhaust collector pipes fitted over the individual engine exhaust stacks.

(Left) The He 111E cockpit was virtually the same for all early He 111s (As through Js). The pilot sat to port and had a control wheel for the elevators and ailerons. This aircraft was modified for pilot training and had duplicate controls fitted in the space normally used for passage to the navigator/bombardier's compartment. The primary interior color for pre-war and early war Luftwaffe aircraft was RLM 02 RLM Gray (FS36165).

(Below) A *Legion Condor* He 111E (25-92) drops 250 KG (551.1 pound) bombs over Republican targets in Spain. These bombs were dropped tail-first from the internal bomb cells. Although the ventral 'dustbin' is lowered, the gunner himself is not in this position. The *Legion Condor* insignia on the tail consisted of a white diving eagle and bomb on a black disc, trimmed in red. (Punka Archiv)

He 111F

In early 1936, Heinkel engineers began redesigning the He 111's wing to simplify its structure and reduce manufacturing time. The elliptical wing was replaced with one with a straight tapered leading edge. This resulted in a slight wingspan reduction from 22.6 M (74 feet 1.8 inches) to 22.5 M (73 feet 9.8 inches); however, the two-spar, three-section wing structure remained unchanged. The aircraft length remained at 17.5 M (57 feet 5 inches), while the height stayed at 4.2 M (13 feet 9.4 inches). During the summer of 1936, an He 111B-0 was equipped with this new wing and was redesignated the **He 111 V7** (D-AUKY). The new straight taper wing was adopted by the He 111G commercial transport, but the RLM (Reich Air Ministry) felt this would impose unacceptable production delays for the bomber version. In the summer of 1937, an He 111B-1 was retrofitted with the new wing and first flew as the **He 111 V11** (D-ARCG) in July of 1937. This aircraft served as the prototype for the **He 111F** series.

The initial **He 111F-0** pre-production aircraft was completed in late 1937. Apart from the wing, this bomber was similar to the previous He 111E series. The new variant was powered by two 1100 HP Junkers Jumo 211A-3 12-cylinder, liquid-cooled, inline engines. These provided greater power than the He 111E-3's 1075 HP Jumo 211A-1s. The aircraft reached a maximum speed of 430 KMH (267.2 MPH) at 5000 M (16,404.2 feet). The He 111F-0 employed an 835 L (220.6 gallon) fuselage bomb bay fuel tank as fitted to the He 111E-5. The additional fuel allowed a maximum range of 1820 KM (1130.9 miles).

In early 1938, Turkey ordered 25 **He 111F-1** bombers (*Werk Nr.* 5013-5037), which were built at Oranienburg. The aircraft were delivered to Turkey during the summer and fall of that year, and remained in Turkish Air Force service until 1946. Heinkel built 20 **He 111F-2**s, which had improved radio equipment. The **He 111F-3** reconnaissance version – equipped with cameras in the bomb bays – was not built. Forty **He 111F-4**s built in mid-1938 had external bomb racks similar to those on the He 111E-4. After briefly serving the Luftwaffe as bombers, they were converted to dual-control trainers. The **He 111F-5** was cancelled on the drawing board, in favor of the improved **He 111P-1**.

This He 111F-1 is parked on a Hungarian airfield in early 1941. The Luftwaffe relegated this aircraft from bombing to training duties by this time. The fuselage code begins NC; however, the rest of this code is unknown. Turkey ordered 25 He 111F-1s, which were delivered by the fall of 1938. (Punka Archiv)

He 111E

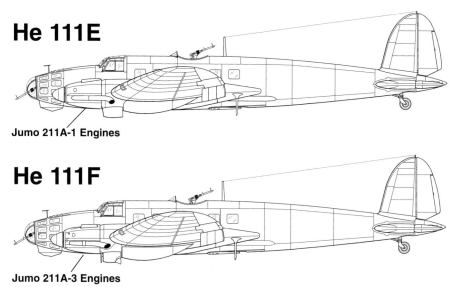

Jumo 211A-1 Engines

He 111F

Jumo 211A-3 Engines

Wing Plan Development

He 111E

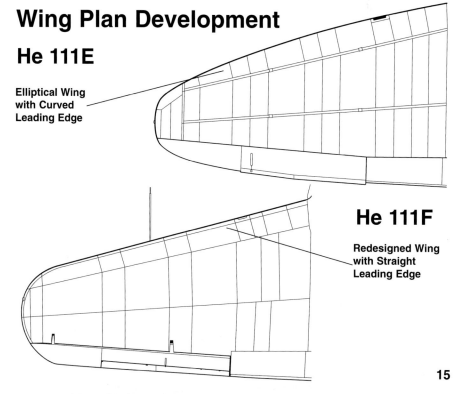

Elliptical Wing with Curved Leading Edge

He 111F

Redesigned Wing with Straight Leading Edge

He 111J

In late 1937, the RLM asked Heinkel to develop a torpedo-carrying variant of the He 111 for the German *Kriegsmarine* (Navy). Heinkel modified two He 111F-4s to meet this requirement. One was redesignated the **He 111 V17** (D-ACBH) and served as the prototype, while the **He 111 V18** (D-ADUM) was used for torpedo carriage and release evaluation. These aircraft were fitted with lower fuselage hardpoints to carry two 765 KG (1686.5 pound) LT F5b[1] torpedoes or 2000 KG (4409.2 pounds) of sea mines. No internal bomb bay was provided on this variant. The aircraft had a maximum weight of 10,600 KG (23,368.6 pounds). Two 1000 HP Daimler-Benz DB 600G 12-cylinder, liquid-cooled, inline engines powered these aircraft, with fixed radiators under the engines. This torpedo bomber was approved for production as the **He 111J** in September of 1938.

Ten pre-production He 111J-0s (*Werk Nr.* 5001-5010) were built in mid 1938. While these aircraft were produced, the *Kriegsmarine* cancelled its torpedo bomber requirement. The 80 subsequent **He 111J-1** production aircraft were built as level bombers for the Luftwaffe, with internal bomb bays installed and external ordnance racks deleted. The He 111J-1 had a maximum speed of 415 KMH (257.9 MPH) at 5000 M (16,404.2 feet) and cruised at 370 KMH (229.9 KMH). Other specifications were the same as for the earlier He 111F. In 1939, the Luftwaffe phased the He 111J-1 from bomber service and employed the surviving aircraft on training duties until 1944.

[1]LT: *Lufttorpedo*, Aerial Torpedo

Two He 111J-1s, including 33+A25 in the foreground, fly in formation during late 1938 or early 1939. These bombers were assigned to KG 4 'General Wever' and were originally built as torpedo-bombers for the Kriegsmarine (German Navy). The Kriegsmarine cancelled its order and the 80 He 111J-1s were reconfigured as level bombers for the Luftwaffe.

One He 111J-1 was fitted with four-bladed propellers for testing purposes. Additional information regarding this test is unknown. Production He 111J-1s had three-bladed VDM variable-pitch propellers, which were turned by 1000 HP DB 611GC engines. (Punka Archiv)

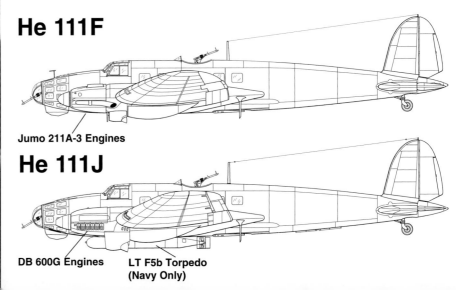

He 111F

Jumo 211A-3 Engines

He 111J

DB 600G Engines

LT F5b Torpedo
(Navy Only)

He 111P

The He 111 was developed for both civilian and military roles; however, nearly all prototypes were for bomber versions. This resulted in Heinkel ending further development of the He 111 in the airliner role in 1937. That same year, Heinkel engineers began studying ways to improve the forward crew's vision and the nose's aerodynamic properties. An He 111B-0 was modified to serve as the **He 111 V8** (D-AQUO), which made its maiden flight from Rostock-Marienehe in January of 1938.

The aircraft's nose was extensively changed from one with a stepped windshield to a heavily glazed nose, offset to starboard. This shorter nose reduced the He 111's overall length from 17.5 M (57 feet 5 inches) to 16.4 M (53 feet 9.7 inches). The pilot sat in the port seat, with the instrument panel mounted on the cockpit roof. This arrangement provided him with great visibility forward and below the aircraft. While landing and taxiing, the pilot could slide the overhead hatch aft and raise his seat. A small folding windshield was extended upward when the pilot's head was above the hatchway.

The navigator/bombardier sat alongside the pilot for takeoff and landing. In flight, he moved to a prone position in the forward nose, which was placed asymmetrically to starboard. This crewman aimed the bombs using a Lotfe C7[1] bombsight, which was mounted in a streamlined fairing on the nose undersurface. The navigator/bombardier also manned a 7.92MM Rheinmetall MG 15 machine gun fitted to a Ikaria GD-A 1114 ball mount (*A-Stand*).

Successful flight tests with the He 111V8 resulted in this same nose being retrofitted to the He 111 V7 in mid-1938. This aircraft had tested the straight tapered wing first used by the He 111F. The He 111 V7 introduced refinements in both the dorsal and ventral gun positions. The dorsal position (*B-Stand*) was widened for improved maneuvering by the radio operator/gunner. A sliding clear plastic hood open to the rear was added over this position, which included one 7.92MM MG 15. A permanent gondola on the centerline replaced the retractable 'dustbin' ventral position (*C-Stand*). This gondola provided the gunner with a 90° field of fire for his MG 15 to protect the He 111's undersurface and tail. The enclosed position also improved the aircraft's aerodynamic characteristics over the drag inducing 'dustbin.' The Luftwaffe felt – based on the *Legion Condor*'s experience against slow and lightly armed fighters over Spain – that only three 7.92MM machine guns were a sufficient defensive armament for the He 111.

The He 111 V7's powerplant consisted of two 1150 HP Daimler-Benz DB 601Aa 12-cylinder, liquid-cooled, inline engines. A supercharger intake duct was mounted on the cowling's port side. Exhausts were vented from the engines through individual stubs mounted along the cowlings. The hydraulically operated main landing gear was modified to withstand higher aircraft weights. A retractable tail wheel replaced the earlier fixed unit to further reduce drag. The Luftwaffe approved the He 111 V7 for production as the **He 111P**, and the first pre-production **He 111P-0**s left Heinkel's Marienehe assembly line – immediately following the last He 111J – in the fall of 1938.

The first 20 production He 111P-1s (*Werk Nr.* 1365-1384) were completed at Marienehe in early 1939. This was several weeks behind schedule, due to the late delivery of engine oil pumps to Heinkel. License production also began at the Norddeutschen Dornier-Werke in Wismar and at Arado's Warnemünde factory. The He 111P-1 entered operational Luftwaffe service with KG 157 in the early spring of 1939, replacing the Wing's older He 111Bs. Insufficient quantities of 1150 HP DB 601Aa engines caused He 111P-1s to be powered by 1100 HP DB 601A-1 engines.

Three factories produced 68 He 111P-1s before production shifted to the **He 111P-2** in May of 1939. This variant was externally identical to the P-1, but replaced the earlier FuG III radio with the more powerful FuG X. Insufficient FuG X production slowed He 111P-2 deliveries by several weeks. Heinkel/Marienehe and Dornier/Wismar built 749 He 111P-2s by July of 1940.

The He 111P-2's wingspan was 22.5 M (73 feet 9.8 inches), with an overall length of 16.4 M (53 feet 9.7 inches) and a height of 4 M (13 feet 1.5 inches). It had an empty weight of 6250

An He 111P-2 is parked outside the Heinkel factory at Rostock-Marienehe in early 1939. The earlier He 111P-1 was the first production variant to feature the redesigned nose, enclosed dorsal gun position, and ventral gondola. The Lotfe C7 bombsight and its fairing are not mounted under the nose of this He 111P-2. No codes were painted on the fuselage and wings of this aircraft.

[1]Lotfe: *Lotfernrohr*, Bomb Sight

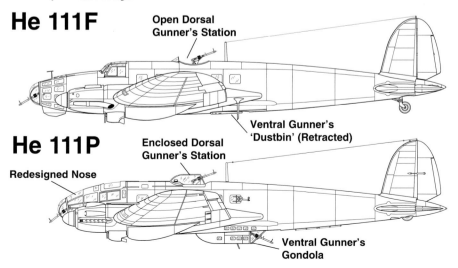

He 111F
Open Dorsal Gunner's Station
Ventral Gunner's 'Dustbin' (Retracted)

He 111P
Enclosed Dorsal Gunner's Station
Redesigned Nose
Ventral Gunner's Gondola

The nose gun position is offset to starboard on the He 111P-2 and subsequent variants. Additional windows on the nose undersurface aided the pilot in taxiing, take off, and landing. Supercharger intakes for the DB 601 engines were mounted on the port cowling sides. The letters HE painted on the starboard wing undersurface are believed to refer to Heinkel.

The *Werk Nummer* (Factory Number) 2616 is white on the mid-fuselage of this He 111P-2. This number was usually painted on the vertical stabilizer, near the rudder hinge. The antenna mast was moved from immediately aft of the cockpit to the upper mid-fuselage. The early narrow *Balkenkreuz* national insignia is painted on this aircraft. All He 111s had all metal structure and covering, except for the fabric-covered control surfaces (rudder, elevators, and ailerons).

KG (13,778.7 pounds) and a maximum take off weight of 12,700 KG (27,998.2 pounds). The powerplant consisted of two 1100 HP Daimler-Benz DB 601A-1 inline engines, which turned VDM three-bladed, variable pitch, metal propellers. The He 111P-2 had a top speed of 410 KMH (254.8 MPH) at 5000 M (16,404.2 feet) and a cruising speed of 380 KMH (236.1 MPH). Its service ceiling was 8000 M (26,246.7 feet) and its maximum range was 1970 KM (1224.1 miles). Four self-sealing fuel tanks were installed in the wings, including two 700 L (184.9 gallon) tanks inboard of the engine nacelles and two 1025 L (270.8 gallon) tanks outboard of these nacelles. These gave the He 111P a total capacity of 3450 L (911.4 gallons) of 87 octane B4 grade fuel.

The bomber could carry a 2000 KG (4409.2 pound) bomb load internally, with eight 250 KG (551.1 pound) weapons vertically mounted in two rows of four bomb stowage cells per row. The He 111P-2 introduced the ESAC250/IX[2] internal bomb rack system, which released the weapons using the RAB 14az automatic consecutive bomb-release mechanism. Its defensive armament consisted of three 7.92MM MG 15 machine guns in single mounts located in the nose, dorsal station, and ventral gondola.

Several He 111P-2s were converted to long-range reconnaissance aircraft by removing their defensive armament and installing cameras inside the bomb bay area. The reconnaissance He 111Ps were powered by two 1175 HP DB 601N engines, which slightly improved its performance over the standard He 111P-2.

Blohm & Voss converted 48 He 111P-1s into **He 111P-3** dual control trainers early in World War Two. These aircraft had their armament and combat equipment removed before they were issued to Luftwaffe advanced flight training schools.

The **He 111P-4** replaced the He 111P-2 in production at the end of 1939. This new variant was powered by two 1100 HP DB 601A-1 engines and had a similar airframe and equipment as the earlier He 111P-2. The He 111P-4 added armor protection for the crew and increased defensive armament, due to higher than expected He 111 losses to enemy fighters during the Polish Campaign in September of 1939. The three 7.92MM MG 15 machine guns (nose, dorsal, and ventral) were supplemented by up to four more weapons. An MG 15 was installed in the front of the ventral gondola and aimed forward. Some crews added another MG 15 to the upper nose, above the Ikaria mount. Some crews also replaced the nose-mounted MG 15 with a 20MM Rheinmetall MG FF cannon. Two MG 15s were placed in side window mounts, one each to port and starboard. A beam gunner was added to the crew for aiming and firing these weapons, increasing the crew to five men. A few He 111P-4s were fitted with a 7.92MM Rheinmetall MG 17 machine gun in the tail cone. This fixed weapon was remotely fired by the dorsal gunner and was intended to discourage attacks from directly aft.

The He 111P-4 replaced the port bomb bay cells with an 835 L (220.6 gallon) fuel tank. This increased the fuel capacity from 3450 L to 4285 L (1132 gallons). Two PVC 1006 external bomb racks were mounted under the fuselage, over the bomb bay doors. Each rack held bombs weighing up to 1000 KG (2204.6 pounds). He 111P-4s sometimes used the ETC 2000[3] external bomb rack, which held one 2500 KG (5511.5 pound) SC 2500[4] bomb. Drag from the external bomb racks reduced the He 111P-4's speed by 35 to 50 KMH (21.7 to 31.1 MPH).

Additional armament and equipment raised the empty weight from the He 111P-2's 6250 KG (13,778.7 pounds) to 6350 KG (13,999.1 pounds) in the He 111P-4. The maximum take off weight went from 12,700 KG (27,998.2 pounds) to 13,500 KG (29,761.9 pounds). This weight increase reduced the He 111P-4's maximum speed to 398 KMH (247.3 MPH) at 5000 M

[2]ESAC: *Elektrische Senkrechtaufhängung für Cylindrischebomben*, Vertical Electric Racks for Cylindrical Bombs
[3]ETC: *Elektrische Trägervorrichtung für Cylindrischebomben*; Electrically Operated Carriers for Cylindrical Bombs
[4]SC: *Splitterbombe Cylindrisch*, Cylindrical Fragmentation Bomb

(16,404.2 feet) and its cruising speed to 370 KMH (229.9 MPH). The additional fuel increased the maximum range to 2450 KM (1522.4 miles), although this was greatly reduced with a 2000 KG bomb load.

Production of 224 He 11P-4s was completed in late 1939 and most surviving aircraft were converted into dual-control trainers by the end of 1943. After completing He 111P-4 production, Heinkel built 24 **He 111P-5**s in late 1939. These were identical to He 111P-4s, apart from slight internal equipment changes. Most He 111P-5s were fitted with two PVC 1006 external bomb racks. Some aircraft were later modified for weather reconnaissance duties, while others were converted to torpedo-bombers.

The **He 111P-6** entered production at Marienehe and Wismar in early 1940. This variant was powered by two 1175 HP Daimler-Benz DB 601N engines. The powerplant raised the aircraft's maximum speed to 440 KMH (273.4 MPH) at 5000 M (16,404.2 feet); however, the increased fuel burn reduced the aircraft's range to 1970 KM (1224.1 miles). The He 111P-6's defensive armament was increased by the installation of 7.92MM Mauser MG 81Z[5] twin-barrel machine guns in the dorsal and ventral positions, with added armor plating on the dorsal gun mount. The dorsal position's plastic canopy was changed to include a three-piece flexible section, which completely enclosed the position. Several He 111P-6s were equipped with glider towing gear under the designation **He 111P-6/R2**.[6]

A few **He 111P-7** and **He 111P-8** aircraft were built in early 1940, primarily for training duties. Heinkel built several **He 111P-9**s – export variants of the He 111P-4 – for the Royal Hungarian Air Force.[7] The Luftwaffe commandeered these aircraft prior to delivery and modified the He 111P-9s for glider towing duties. Hungary received ten He 111P-6s from Luftwaffe stocks in 1942, deploying them in the long-range reconnaissance role. Heinkel at

[5]Z: *Zwilling*, Twin

[6]R: *Rüstatz*, Field Conversion Set

[7]Royal Hungarian Air Force: in Hungarian, *Magyar Királyi Honvéd Légierö* (MKHL)

This He 111P-2 (*Werk Nr.* 2508) has the Nazi flag painted across the vertical tail surfaces. This marking was reduced to a white-trimmed black swastika when the aircraft entered operational service. The pilot sets the trim tabs fitted to the rudder and elevator trailing edges from the cockpit. These tabs hold the rudder and elevator in the desired setting in flight.

Factory technicians install the port DB 601Aa engine on an He 111P-2. The powerplants were placed on engine support mounts, which were attached to the firewall. Heinkel, Dornier, and Arado built He 111Ps – the latter two companies under license from Heinkel. The Luftwaffe had 349 He 111Ps – including 295 serviceable aircraft – when Germany invaded Poland on 1 September 1939. (Petrick)

An He 111P-2 is prepared for flight testing at the factory. Access panels are removed from the DB 601Aa engines for pre-flight servicing. This 12-cylinder, liquid-cooled, inline engine was rated at 1150 HP for take off and 1020 HP at 4500 M (14,763.8 feet). He 111A through H-5 aircraft were equipped with three-bladed variable pitch VDM propellers. (Petrick)

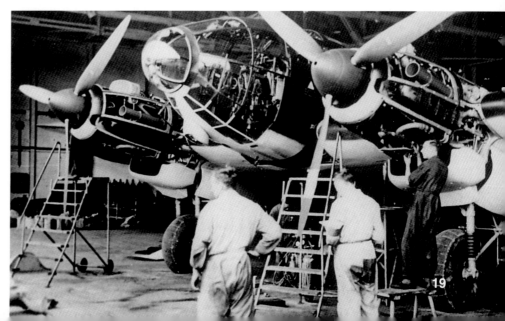

Several He 111Ps approach the final assembly section at a German factory in 1939. Other aircraft move in the opposite direction to be mated with the wing assemblies later in the production line. Production of the Jumo 211-powered He 111H began concurrently with the He 111P, although at different factories. (Werkfoto via Petrick)

An He 111P (NA+IT, *Werk Nr.* 2921) undergoes final assembly at Heinkel's Rostock-Marienehe factory. White radio codes were painted at the factory, then were repainted in *Staffel* colors when delivered to their units. He 115 floatplanes are being assembled alongside the He 111 bombers. (Werkfoto via Petrick)

Rostock-Marienehe constructed 451 of the 739 He 111Ps built between late 1938 and early 1940. The remaining 288 aircraft were split between Norddeutschen-Dornier Werke/Wismar and Arado/Warnemünde.

Two He 111P-1s fly a training mission in mid-1939. A Peil EP direction finding loop antenna is mounted on the upper fuselage, aft of the dorsal gunner's position. This antenna was changed to a Peil G5 in the He 111P-2. The near aircraft's fuselage code is believed to be 25+E33, which indicated a bomber assigned to III/KG 255. The code's first digit indicated the *Luftkreis* (Air Area) and the second denoted the *Geschwader's* numerical position within the *Luftkreis*. The letter indicated that this machine was the fifth aircraft within the *Staffel*. The final two digits showed the aircraft's *Gruppe* (Group) within the Geschwader and its *Staffel* within the *Gruppe*. This code system was replaced by a four letter system from early 1939. (Punka Archiv)

The He 111P's defensive armament included one 7.92MM Rheinmetall MG 15 machine gun in the nose. This weapon was placed in an Ikaria GD-A 1114 ball mount similar to those fitted to earlier He 111 variants. The MG 15 was 108 CM (42.5 inches long), weighed 7.1 KG (15.75 pounds), and had a rate of fire of 1100 rounds per minute. Ammunition was fed from 75-round drums clipped to the breech. (ECPA)

Nose Development

He 111F

Separate Navigator/Bombardier's Compartment

7.92MM MG 15 Machine Gun in GD-A 1114 Ball Mount

Bombsight Housing

Stepped Windshield and Canopy for Pilot

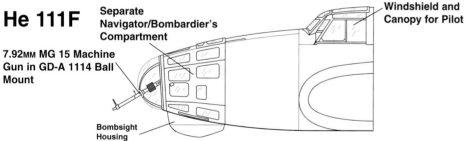

He 111P

Navigator/Bombardier's Section Integral with Nose and Offset to Starboard

Pilot's Canopy Faired with Nose, Offset to Port

Modified Bombsight Housing

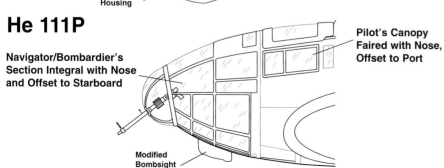

A factory technician works in the cockpit of an He 111P-2 on the assembly line. The pilot was seated to starboard and his main instrument panel was mounted on the ceiling. Flight instruments were located on the panel's port side, while engine instruments were placed to starboard. The control column was mounted on the center, while the control grips were placed on a swing over arm to port. Early in World War Two, German cockpit interiors were changed from RLM 02 RLM Gray (FS36165) to RLM 66 Black Gray (FS36081). (Werkfoto via Petrick)

The dorsal gunner's canopy is mostly closed on this KG 55 He 111P-2, which operated from northern France during late 1940. The closed canopy greatly reduced the radio operator/gunner's exposure to the airstream. It opened to allow the gunner to escape in an emergency. One 7.92MM MG 15 was mounted in this position.

The ventral gunner enters the He 111P's gondola prior to a mission over Poland in 1939. One 7.92MM MG 15 was fitted to the aft window, allowing for protection of the bomber's rear and lower areas. The weapon is fitted with a post-and-ring gunsight, with the post near the breech and the ring near the muzzle. (Bundesarchiv)

Dorsal Gun Position Development

Ventral Gun Position Development

He 111F

He 111F

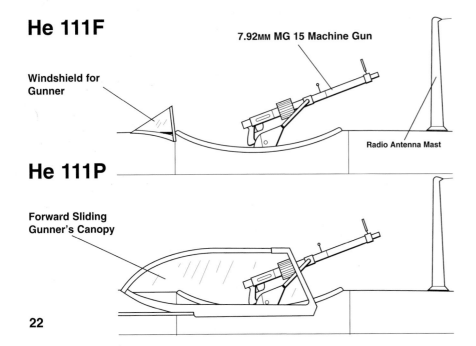

7.92MM MG 15 Machine Gun

Windshield for Gunner

Radio Antenna Mast

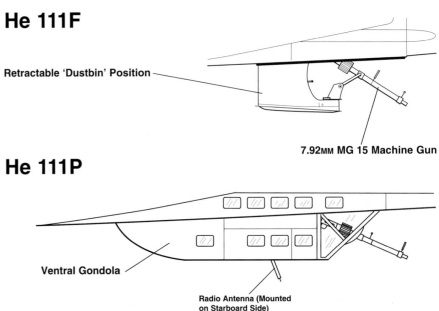

Retractable 'Dustbin' Position

7.92MM MG 15 Machine Gun

He 111P

He 111P

Forward Sliding Gunner's Canopy

Ventral Gondola

Radio Antenna (Mounted on Starboard Side)

Luftwaffe armorers load two 1000 KG (2204.6 pound) SC 1000 bombs onto an He 111P prior to a mission over England in 1940. Each weapon was carried on ETC 2000 external bomb racks fitted to the fuselage undersurface. These racks covered the internal bomb cells, but allowed the He 111 to carry larger and heavier ordnance. (Bundesarchiv)

He 111 Bombs and External Bomb Racks

250 KG (551.1 pound) SC 250 Bomb

1000 KG (2204.6 pound) SC 1000 Bomb

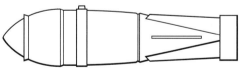

ETC 2000 External Bomb Rack

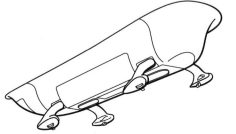

PVC 1006 External Bomb Rack

Armorers load 250 KG (551.1 pound) SC 250 bombs into an He 111P during the 1939 Polish Campaign. The bombs were loaded nose up into the eight ESAC bomb cells – two rows of four cells each. These cells allowed the He 111 to carry its bomb load internally; however, this restricted the weapons' size to 250 KG. A spoiler lowered between the two doors of the front cells to reduce airflow interference with weapons release. (Bundesarchiv)

He 111H-1 through H-5

In 1938, Heinkel simultaneously planned He 111 variants powered by Daimler-Benz DB 601 and Junkers Jumo 211 inline engines. The He 111P series used the DB 601, but this power-plant was in high demand for Messerschmitt's Bf 109 and Bf 110 fighters. The Jumo 211-pow-ered He 111 with the revised nose was first tested on the **He 111 V19** (D-AUKY) prototype, which first flew in January of 1939. This aircraft was identical to the He 111P-2, apart from the two 1010 HP Jumo 211A-1 12-cylinder, liquid-cooled, inline engines. This engine's super-charger intake was mounted to starboard, instead of the DB 601's port side installation.

The Luftwaffe soon approved the He 111 V19 for production as the **He 111H**, and Heinkel built 25 **He 111H-0** pre-production aircraft at its Oranienburg factory by the following May. This was immediately followed by the initial production variant, the **He 111H-1**. Junkers had intended to build this model at its Dessau plant; however, demand for its Ju 88 bomber result-ed in the He 111H-1 license being switched to ATG in Leipzig. Production was hampered by shortages of critical components, including ESAC bomb racks, RAB bomb release mecha-nisms, and FuG X radios. This situation resulted in these items being stripped from Junkers Ju 52/3m 'auxiliary bombers' in Luftwaffe service. Nevertheless, Heinkel and ATG combined to produce 136 He 111H-1s (116 by Heinkel and 20 by ATG) by the fall of 1939.

The He 111H-1 had a maximum speed of 425 KMH (264.1 MPH) without a bomb load, which was a maximum of 2000 KG (4409.2 pounds). This load consisted of eight 250 KG (551.1 pound) or thirty-two 50 KG (110.2 pound) weapons loaded nose up into the eight bomb bay cells. Three 7.92MM Rheinmetall MG 15 machine guns were installed in single mounts in the nose, dorsal, and ventral positions (*A-*, *B-*, and *C-Stands*, respectively).

A soldier looking through his periscope sees an He 111H-1 taking off from France in mid-1940. Early He 111Hs were nearly identical to He 111Ps, but were powered by Jumo 211 engines. These powerplants had the supercharger intakes to starboard, instead of the port-mounted scoops used by the He 111P's DB 601 engines. (Bundesarchiv)

This variant had identical external dimensions to the He 111P series. It had a wingspan of 22.5 M (73 feet 9.8 inches), an overall length of 16.4 M (53 feet 9.7 inches), and a height of 4 M (13 feet 1.5 inches). The He 111H-1 weighed 6300 KG (13,888.9 pounds) empty and 12,600 KG (27,777.8 pounds) fully loaded for take off. Its service ceiling was 8000 M (26,246.7 feet) and its maximum range was 2060 KM (1280.1 miles). Four self-sealing fuel tanks containing 3450 L (911.4 gallons) of 87 octane B4 grade fuel were fitted into the wings. The He 111H-1 had a four-man crew: pilot, bombardier/navigator, radio operator/dorsal gunner, and ventral gunner.

He 111H-1 production yielded to the **He 111H-2** in September of 1939. This was identical to the previous variant, but was powered by 1100 HP Jumo 211A-3 engines. A lengthened supercharger air intake was fitted to the starboard nacelle sides, compared to the duct used by He 111H-1s. He 111H-2 defensive armament was originally the same as for the He 111H-1, but this was increased in October of 1939. Two MG 15s were added to the fuselage beam posi-tions – one weapon each to port and to starboard – with a beam gunner added to the crew. A single MG 15 was mounted to the forward ventral gondola. Three He 111H-2s were used to test bombing equipment and defensive armament. The **He 111H-2/R1** was a sub-variant used to train crews in anti-shipping operations. Heinkel and ATG built 502 He 111H-2s before the end of 1939.

The first **He 111H-3** was rolled out from the production line in November of 1939. This vari-ant employed two 1200 HP Jumo 211D-1 engines and was intended for both level bombing and anti-shipping missions. Armor plating was added to the crew stations and a second MG 15 was mounted in the upper nose. Several He 111H-3s had the front gondola MG 15 replaced by a 20MM MG FF cannon. Some He 111H-3 crews modified their aircraft in the field to carry a MG FF in the nose and a 7.92MM MG 17 machine gun in the tail cone. A sixth crewman was sometimes carried to help coordinate attacks on enemy shipping. Heinkel built 182 He 111H-3s at Oranienburg, while Arado/Brandenburg completed 196 aircraft and ATG/Leipzig built 126 machines. This resulted in 504 He 111H-3s completed through early 1940.

The **He 111H-4** replaced the He 111H-3 in production in early 1940. It was nearly identical

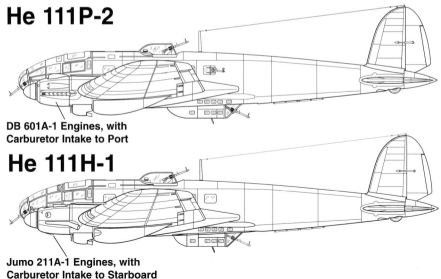

He 111P-2

DB 601A-1 Engines, with Carburetor Intake to Port

He 111H-1

Jumo 211A-1 Engines, with Carburetor Intake to Starboard

to the preceding variant, but with the option of replacing its four port bomb compartments with an 835 L (220.6 gallon) fuel tank. The four starboard compartments were retained for bomb delivery. PVC 1006 and ETC 2000 external bomb racks were often mounted over the bomb compartment doors to carry large bombs, torpedoes, or mines. Early He 111H-4s had Jumo 211D-1 engines, but later aircraft were powered by 1400 HP Jumo 211F-1 engines. Heinkel, Arado, and ATG combined to build 150 He 111H-4s by early 1941.

The **He 111H-5** retained the He 111H-4's airframe, while modifying its offensive and defensive armament. Internal bomb carriage was seldom used, since most offensive ordnance was carried on ETC 2000 and/or PVC 1006 external racks. It could carry a bomb or torpedo on one rack and an auxiliary fuel tank on the other rack. The He 111H-5 carried two 765 KG (1686.5 pound) LT F5b or LT F5W torpedoes for attacking surface vessels. Other combinations included a 1000 KG (2204.6 pound) SC 1000 bomb, four 250 KG (551.1 pound) SC 250 bombs, or six 50 KG (110.2 pound) LC 50F flare bombs. The ETC 2000 rack allowed this aircraft to carry one 2500 KG (5511.5 pound) SC 2500 bomb.

Armor plating was fitted over the ventral gondola windows, while the lenticular (double convex) armored glass gun mount was replaced by a simpler clear plastic mount. The 7.92MM MG 15 machine gun was mounted on an articulated suspension, which allowed easier movement and an increased angle of fire over the previous mounting.

Some He 111H-5s were configured for reconnaissance missions, equipped with Rb 50/30[1] and Rb 20/30 cameras in the port bomb bay. Six 50 KG LC 50F flare bombs for night photography were carried on an ETC 2000 rack mounted to starboard. Exhaust flame dampers for night operations were fitted to this and other He 111 variants from the fall of 1940.

The **He 111H-5/R1** subvariant received modified FT radio equipment, while the **He 111H-5/R2** replaced the gondola-mounted 20MM MG FF with a 7.92MM MG 15. Aircraft equipped with PVC 1006 external bomb racks were designated **He 111H-5/R3**s, while **He 111H-5/R-4**s had both internal and external bomb carriage.

The He 111H-5's weight increased to 6950 KG (15,321.9 pounds) empty and 15,700 KG (34,612 pounds) at take off. To meet this increased weight, the main landing gear was strengthened and its tires were enlarged. Tire size increased from 1100MM (43.3 inches) in diameter by 375MM (14.8 inches) wide to 1400MM (55.1 inches) by 410MM (16.1 inches). The maximum speed fell to 405 KMH (251.7 MPH); however, the additional fuel increased its range to 3100 KM (1926.3 miles).

Factories at Oranienburg (Heinkel), Brandenburg (Arado), and Leipzig (ATG) produced 175 He 111H-5s by August of 1940 and approximately 500 aircraft by the end of 1941. Hungary ordered 20 He 111H-5s in late 1940; however, they never arrived in Hungary. The Luftwaffe requisitioned these aircraft for use in the invasion of the Soviet Union (Operation BARBAROSSA) on 22 June 1941.

[1]Rb: *Reihenbildkamera*, Automatic Aerial Camera

He 111H-3

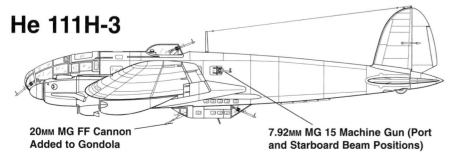

20MM MG FF Cannon Added to Gondola

7.92MM MG 15 Machine Gun (Port and Starboard Beam Positions)

This He 111H-2 (T5+AU) is parked on a snow-covered German airfield during the winter of 1939-40. The aircraft was assigned to the *Wettererkundungstaffel Ob.d.L.* (Long-Range Weather Reconnaissance Squadron of the Air Force Commander-in-Chief). This unit reported directly to Luftwaffe Headquarters and provided weather data to mission planners. The white code letter A on the outboard wing tips was overpainted with a dark green paint. (Punka Archiv)

An He 111H-2 (A1+BA) assigned to *Stab* (Staff)/KG 53 '*Legion Condor'* flies with five other He 111s over France in 1940. Three white vertical bars were painted on the rudder of KG 53's aircraft during the Battle of Britain. These markings aided in assembling large bomber formations. Additional 7.92MM MG 15s were fitted to the upper nose and front gondola positions (Löhr)

This early He 111H was assigned to *Wekusta* 5 (*Wettererkundungstaffel*; Long-Range Weather Reconnaissance Squadron) early in World War Two. The Lotfe C7A bomb sight and its fairing were removed from under the starboard nose, while a barometer was mounted under the port nose. *Wekusta* 5's winged frog insignia is painted on the fuselage side. (Löhr)

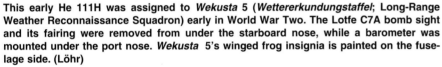

A navigator/bombardier crouches behind the nose-mounted 7.92ᴍᴍ MG 15 in his He 111H prior to a mission. The Ikaria ball mount allowed for considerable movement while keeping the machine gun firmly within the nose. A second MG 15 was installed in the upper nose of this aircraft. (Bundesarchiv)

The bombardier/navigator checks his equipment aboard an He 111H prior to a mission. He lays on his stomach while aiming and firing the nose-mounted 7.92ᴍᴍ MG 15. A chute for collecting spent cartridges is fitted below the machine gun's breech. The pilot's rudder pedals are mounted off the forward edge of the cockpit floor, along the port nose side.

A Luftwaffe ground crewman lies atop this He 111H's canopy, while a colleague services the cockpit. The bombardier/navigator's starboard canopy panel was removed for servicing. The upper port canopy slid aft for pilot's access. It also opened for taxiing, take offs, and landings. The pilot raised his seat so his head appeared above the canopy for improved visibility during these times. A small retractable windshield opened forward during this procedure.

A gunner stands by the mid-fuselage of his He 111H, which landed at its home airfield despite battle damage. One 7.92MM MG 15 was mounted in the aft starboard window; another MG 15 was fitted to the opposite window. Shrapnel damage from anti-aircraft fire occurred above the next window on the starboard side. (Punka Archiv)

The gunner aims one of the two beam-mounted MG 15s at enemy fighters. One gunner was responsible for both the port and starboard beam machine guns. The window was sealed shut, which limited the beam guns' fields of fire compared to open windows. Each MG 15 was provided with 75-round ammunition drums, which were clipped to the breech. The use of these drums made the MG 15 slower to reload versus using belted ammunition.

An MG 15 juts out of the port beam window on this He 111H-2 (T5+FU) of *Wekusta Ob.d.L.* The aircraft retained their defensive armament despite their weather reconnaissance tasking. The He 111's minimal defensive armament was slightly improved in effectiveness by close formation flights. This allowed the gunners to bring more weapons to bear against enemy fighters. (Punka Archiv)

An He 111H-3 (1G+HP) of I *Gruppe*/KG 27 flies over the Eastern Front during the latter half of 1941. This aircraft was retrofitted with a 20MM MG FF cannon in the nose for increased defensive firepower. The cannon was designed by Switzerland's Oerlikon and built in Germany by Rheinmetall. The aft fuselage band was RLM 27 Yellow (FS33637) on Axis aircraft operating over the Eastern Front from June of 1941. (Schmidt)

Nose with Two 7.92MM MG 15 Machine Guns

Nose with One 20MM MG FF Cannon

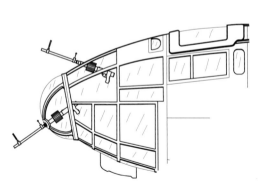

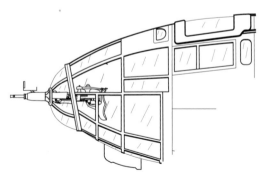

7.92MM MG 15

20MM MG FF

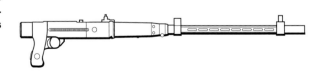

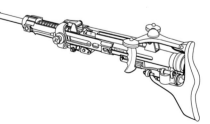

This He 111H-3 is equipped with two 7.92MM MG 15s in the nose. One is mounted in the standard Ikaria GD-A 1114 mount in the extreme nose, while an additional weapon was fitted to the upper nose. Luftwaffe maintenance depots added the second nose gun to some He 111s from mid-1940 for additional defensive armament. The bombardier/navigator's horizontal pad ends near the Ikaria mounted MG 15. (Mészáros)

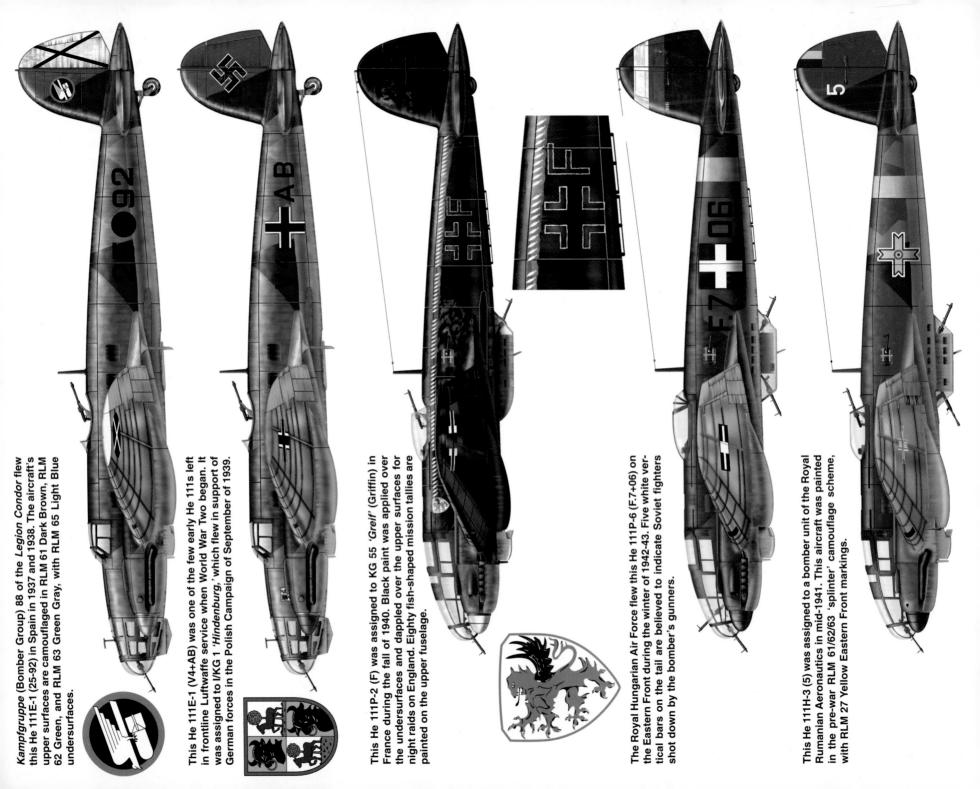

Kampfgruppe (Bomber Group) 88 of the *Legion Condor* flew this He 111E-1 (25-92) in Spain in 1937 and 1938. The aircraft's upper surfaces are camouflaged in RLM 61 Dark Brown, RLM 62 Green, and RLM 63 Green Gray, with RLM 65 Light Blue undersurfaces.

This He 111E-1 (V4+AB) was one of the few early He 111s left in frontline Luftwaffe service when World War Two began. It was assigned to I/KG 1 '*Hindenburg*,' which flew in support of German forces in the Polish Campaign of September of 1939.

This He 111P-2 (F) was assigned to KG 55 '*Greif*' (Griffin) in France during the fall of 1940. Black paint was applied over the undersurfaces and dappled over the upper surfaces for night raids on England. Eighty fish-shaped mission tallies are painted on the upper fuselage.

The Royal Hungarian Air Force flew this He 111P-6 (F.7+06) on the Eastern Front during the winter of 1942-43. Five white vertical bars on the tail are believed to indicate Soviet fighters shot down by the bomber's gunners.

This He 111H-3 (5) was assigned to a bomber unit of the Royal Rumanian Aeronautics in mid-1941. This aircraft was painted in the pre-war RLM 61/62/63 'splinter' camouflage scheme, with RLM 27 Yellow Eastern Front markings.

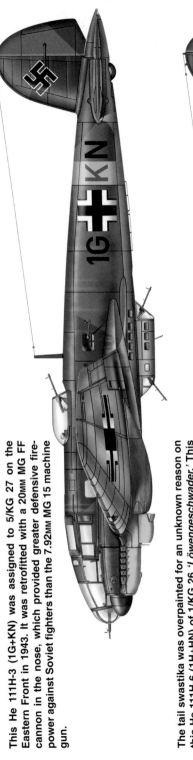

This He 111H-3 (1G+KN) was assigned to 5/KG 27 on the Eastern Front in 1943. It was retrofitted with a 20mm MG FF cannon in the nose, which provided greater defensive firepower against Soviet fighters than the 7.92mm MG 15 machine gun.

The tail swastika was overpainted for an unknown reason on this He 111H-6 (1H+HN) of 1/KG 26 'Löwengeschwader.' This Squadron flew from Stavanger-Sola, Norway during the Battle of Britain.

This He 111H-6 (1H+GP) of 6/KG 26 flew anti-shipping missions from Italy during the summer of 1942. Aircraft of II Gruppe used a yellow background on the Wing's insignia. The port LT F5b torpedo obscures the 20mm MG FF mounted in the front of the ventral gondola.

The 2 Staffel of Schleppgruppe (Towing Group) 4 flew this He 111H-16 (NI+JE) on the Eastern Front during the winter of 1942-43. Temporary white paint was applied over the standard RLM 70 Black Green and RLM 71 Dark Green upper surface finish.

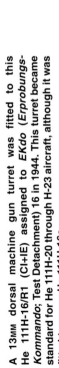

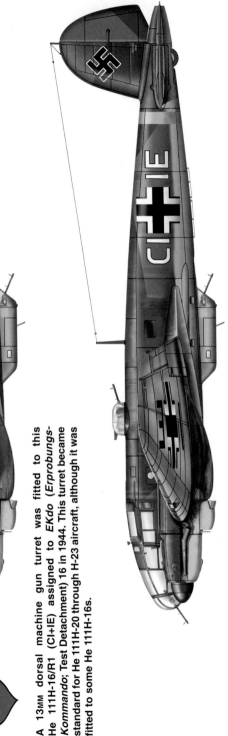

A 13mm dorsal machine gun turret was fitted to this He 111H-16/R1 (CI+IE) assigned to EKdo (Erprobungs-Kommando; Test Detachment) 16 in 1944. This turret became standard for He 111H-20 through H-23 aircraft, although it was fitted to some He 111H-16s.

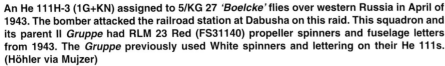

An He 111H-3 (1G+KN) assigned to 5/KG 27 *'Boelcke'* flies over western Russia in April of 1943. The bomber attacked the railroad station at Dabusha on this raid. This squadron and its parent II *Gruppe* had RLM 23 Red (FS31140) propeller spinners and fuselage letters from 1943. The *Gruppe* previously used White spinners and lettering on their He 111s. (Höhler via Mujzer)

This He 111H-4 (1T+AA) was assigned to *Stab*/KG 28 during 1942. The ventral gondola access door was removed from this aircraft for an unknown reason. The Squadron identification letter A was RLM 24 Dark Blue (FS25053), while the other lettering was black. No war theater band was painted on this He 111. (Dr. Volker Koos)

An He 111H-3 is parked ahead of the Gotha Go 242 transport glider it will tow on its next mission over the Eastern Front. Many He 111Hs were modified with glider towing equipment in the tail cone. This mission increased in importance as the war continued. The Go 242 had a two-man crew and held either 21 troops with their full equipment or 2500 KG (5511.5 pounds) of cargo. (Jules Bernard)

Field Marshal Erwin Rommel, commander of the *Deutsche Afrika Korps*, used this He 111H-4 (VG+ES, *Werk Nr.* 4085) as his transport. The aircraft's upper surfaces were painted RLM 79 Sand Yellow (FS30215) and RLM 80 Olive Green (FS34052), with RLM 78 Light Blue (FS35352) undersurfaces. The aft fuselage band and letters are white, while E and part of S are outlined in RLM 23 Red. (Schmidt)

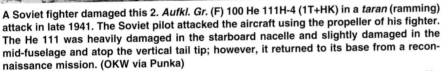

A Soviet fighter damaged this 2. *Aufkl. Gr.* (F) 100 He 111H-4 (1T+HK) in a *taran* (ramming) attack in late 1941. The Soviet pilot attacked the aircraft using the propeller of his fighter. The He 111 was heavily damaged in the starboard nacelle and slightly damaged in the mid-fuselage and atop the vertical tail tip; however, it returned to its base from a reconnaissance mission. (OKW via Punka)

An He 111H-5 (1H+BK) assigned to 2/KG 26 *'Löwengeschwader'* flies a mission over Norway in 1941. Larger crosses on the wing undersurfaces were overpainted with RLM 65 Light Blue and regulation-sized national insignia painted on the wing. The propeller spinners are RLM 23 Red (FS31140), which was 2 Staffel's color. (Punka Archiv)

Armorers laid out 50 KG (110.2 pound) bombs near an He 111H-4 of 1/KG 27 *'Boelcke,'* which is parked at an airfield in Russia during the winter of 1941-42. The nose-mounted 20MM MG FF cannon had a muzzle velocity of 550 M (1804.5 feet) per second and a firing rate of 450 rounds per minute. The Germans temporarily painted the upper surfaces white for camouflage against the snow-covered landscape. (Löhr)

This He 111H-5 is armed with a 20MM MG FF cannon in the nose Ikaria mount, while an additional 7.92MM MG 15 machine gun is installed on the upper nose. Early He 111H-5s often carried the nose-mounted cannon for attacking surface targets at low altitude. A spent cartridge bag is mounted under the MG FF's breech. (Petrick)

Luftwaffe ground crewmen bring 500 KG (1102.3 pound) SC 500 bombs to an He 111H-5 at a German airfield in France. The bombs were mounted on ETC 2000 bomb racks fitted to the fuselage over the internal bomb bay doors. The He 111's undersurfaces are over-painted black for night bombing missions. (Punka Archiv)

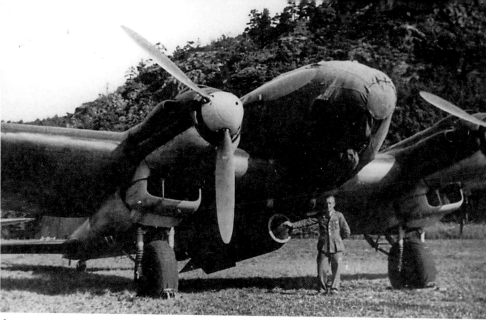

A crewman stands under an I/KG 26 He 111H at an airfield in Norway during the summer of 1940. His right hand rests on a 1000 KG (2204.6 pound) SC 1000 'Hermann' bomb. An He 111 carried only one of these 2.8 M (9.2 foot) long weapons, whose explosions left craters 10 M (32.8 feet) deep. Canvas covers were placed over the He 111H's nose glazing. (Kovács)

An He 111H-5 (1H+FH) of I/KG 26 flies with an 1000 KG SC 1000 'Hermann' bomb under the fuselage. The weapon was carried on a PVC 1006 bomb rack offset to port. Its nickname of 'Hermann' was prompted by the bomb's large girth, which reminded airmen of *Reichsmarshall* Hermann Göring, the Luftwaffe's rotund Commander-in-Chief. A radio antenna is mounted immediately to starboard of the ventral gondola and extended down to allow sufficient signal coverage. The propeller spinners and the aircraft code letter F are white, the color of I *Gruppe*. (Schmidt)

He 111H-6 through H-15

The **He 111H-6** incorporated changes made to earlier He 111H-3s and H-5s based on operational experience. This new variant combined the He 111H-5 airframe with two 1300 HP Junkers Jumo 211F-1 12-cylinder, liquid-cooled, inline engines. These engines turned VDM three-bladed narrow-chord (width), variable pitch, metal propellers. Late production aircraft received the 1340 HP Jumo 211F-2, which turned three-bladed wooden Junkers VS11 variable pitch propellers. These wider chord propellers – each within an enlarged spinner – became standard on subsequent He 111s. He 111H-6 production began in June of 1941.

This variant had a wingspan of 22.5 M (73 feet 9.8 inches), a length of 16.4 M (53 feet 9.7 inches), and a height of 4 M (13 feet 1.5 inches). The Jumo 211F-2-powered He 111H-6 had a maximum speed of 435 KMH (270.3 MPH), which was reduced by 30 to 35 KMH (18.6 to 21.7 MPH) when external bomb racks were installed. It had a maximum ceiling of 8500 M (27,887.1 feet), which was reduced to 6500 M (21,325.5 feet) with external racks. Wing and fuselage tanks held 4285 L (1132 gallons) of fuel and 300 L (79.3 gallons) of oil. Fuel capacity was reduced to 3450 L (911.4 gallons) when the bomb bays were used for ordnance. The aircraft had a range of 2500 KM (1553.5 miles) with full fuel capacity and 1800 KM (1118.5 miles) with the bomb bay tank removed. This variant had a maximum take off weight of 14,000 KG (30,864.2 pounds). Early aircraft had FuG X, Peil-GV, and FuB1 radios, which were superceded by FuG 16 and FuG 28 units by early 1941. Some He 111H-6s were equipped with an FuG 101a radio altimeter.

The He 111H-6 was armed with six 7.92MM Rheinmetall MG 15 machine guns in single mounts. One was in the nose Ikaria GD-A 1114 mounting (*A-Stand*), another was in the dorsal mount (*B-Stand*), one each were fitted to the port and starboard fuselage sides, and two were fitted to the ventral gondola (*C-Stand*) – one forward and one aft. Some crews replaced the nose and forward gondola weapons with 20MM Rheinmetall MG FF cannon, which were primarily used against surface targets. Additionally, some aircraft had a 7.92MM Rheinmetall MG 17 fixed in the tail cone and remotely controlled from the dorsal gun position. A few aircraft were fitted with a tube for launching grenades at enemy fighters, but this proved unsuccessful.

The first 500 He 111H-6s were equipped with an ETC 2000 bomb rack to port and a PVC 1006L rack to starboard. Later aircraft had ETC 2000s on both port and starboard sides. ESAC internal bomb racks were another option, which required deletion of the fuselage fuel tank. This variant could carry two 1800 KG (3968.3 pound) SC 1800 bombs or two 765 KG (1686.5 pound) LT F5b or LT F5W torpedoes externally.

The He 111H-6 was the most produced variant of Heinkel's medium bomber. Heinkel, Arado, and ATG produced approximately 1800 aircraft between May of 1941 and the end of 1942. He 111H-6s saw service on all fronts as level bombers, torpedo bombers, reconnaissance aircraft, transports, and mine layers.

The **He 111H-7** was a proposed night bomber variant based on the He 111H-6. It would have removed some of its defensive armament and armor plating and control the remaining defensive armament using remote control. This proposal was rejected in November of 1941 and the aircraft was cancelled.

Heinkel converted 30 He 111H-3s and H-5s to **He 111H-8** standard in early 1941. This variant was equipped with cable cutting gear to counter the low-flying barrage balloons used to help defend British cities and targets. A large balloon cable cutter weighing 1000 KG (2204.6 pounds) was mounted on frames secured to the nose and wing leading edges, while ballast in the tail countered the cutting gear's weight. This additional weight reduced the He 111H-8's offensive load to 1000 KG, while the increased drag reduced its performance and handling. This program was cancelled after a brief service career and the 20 surviving He 111H-8s were converted to glider tugs under the designation **He 111H-8/R2**. The **He 111H-9** was an

An He 111H-6 (A1+EB) assigned to KG 53 *'Legion Condor'* flies over western Europe in mid-1940. This bomber was assigned to the *Stab* (Staff) Flight of the Wing's I *Gruppe* and had its individual code letter E in RLM 25 Light Green (FS34115). KG 53 was descended from the *Legion Condor* deployed to Spain during its Civil War. (Punka Archiv)

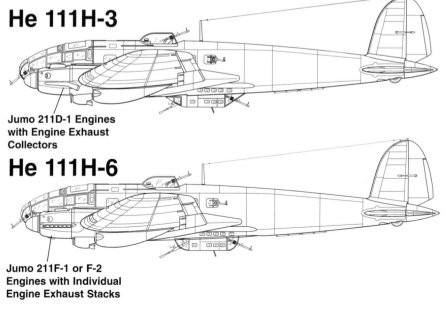

He 111H-3

Jumo 211D-1 Engines with Engine Exhaust Collectors

He 111H-6

Jumo 211F-1 or F-2 Engines with Individual Engine Exhaust Stacks

He 111H-6 with slight changes in its internal equipment and was only produced in small quantities.

The Germans converted 425 early He 111Hs into **He 111H-10** night bombers from late 1941. This variant was powered by 1300 HP Jumo 211F-1 engines, whose exhausts were shrouded by exhaust flame dampers. The dampers hid exhaust flames from enemy eyes in the air and on the surface. A *Kuto-Nase* (Nose Cutter) balloon cable cutter was installed on the nose and two *Kuto* cutters were fitted to the wing leading edges. This installation was considerably lighter than the large cable cutter used by the earlier He 111H-8. Emergency fuel dump tubes were installed on the wing undersurfaces ahead of the ailerons.

In the summer of 1942, Heinkel and the RLM decided to decrease He 111 production in favor of newer aircraft. The program called for a run down of He 111H-6 production, while one-third of further production was to be of the **He 111H-11** and two-thirds to be of the **He 111H-14**. The He 111H-11 was based on the He 111H-3, but with revised defensive armament and more powerful engines. The dorsal gun position (*B-Stand*) was fully enclosed and had more armor protection, while its 7.92MM MG 15 machine gun was replaced by a 13MM Rheinmetall MG 131 machine gun. The dorsal radio antenna mast was repositioned slightly aft to provide clearance for this weapon. A 20MM MG FF cannon replaced the nose-mounted 7.92MM MG 15 machine gun (*A-Stand*). The single MG 15 fitted to the aft gondola position (*C-Stand*) was replaced by a 7.92MM Mauser MG 81Z twin-barrel machine gun. The beam positions originally retained the single MG 15s, but **He 111H-11/R1**s replaced these with MG 81Zs. This revised armament was standardized on He 111H-11s by November of 1942, although some units replaced the MG FFs with MG 131s in the field. These crews preferred the MG 131's higher rate of fire over that of the MG FF. The port internal ESAC bomb racks could be removed and an 835 L (220.6 gallon) fuel tank installed in their place. Many He 111H-11s were equipped with a new PVC rack under the fuselage, which carried five 250 KG (551.1 pound) bombs. Additional armor plating was fitted around crew spaces. Some of this plating was placed on the lower fuselage and could be jettisoned to lighten the aircraft in emergency situations.

The He 111H-11's powerplant consisted of two 1340 HP Junkers Jumo 211F-2 engines. These engines allowed this variant to carry a 2000 KG (4409.2 pound) payload to a range of 2340 KM (1454 miles). The He 111H-11 was built in torpedo bomber and level bomber/mine layer sub-variants. Some aircraft were fitted with glider towing gear and were redesignated **He 111H-11/R2**s. Several aircraft were equipped with *Kuto-Nase* and *Kuto* cable cutters. Heinkel converted 100 He 111H-3s to H-11 standard and built 230 new aircraft by the summer of 1943.

In late 1942, Heinkel developed the **He 111H-12** for carrying and launching Air-to-Surface Missiles (ASMs). This aircraft was based on the He 111H-11, but deleted the ventral gondola and reduced the crew to four men. The 37 He 111H-12s built each carried two Henschel Hs 293A missiles under the wings, which the bombardier guided to the target. These tests were inconclusive and this variant did not see operational service. There was no **He 111H-13** variant.

The **He 111H-14** combined the He 111H-10 airframe with Jumo 211F-2 engines and improved navigation equipment. This variant was intended for the pathfinder role in night bombing raids. The navigation equipment enabled its crew to drop its bomb load without visual contact of their target. Bombs were carried in either eight ESAC internal racks or four ESAC racks and one ETC 2000 external rack. The 50 He 111H-14s built primarily served in western Europe during 1944. The **He 111H-15** was an He 111H-12 intended to carry two Blohm & Voss BV 246 gliding bombs for precision stand-off attacks. Tests demonstrated the BV 246's low accuracy, which resulted in this variant's cancellation.

A 5/KG 26 *'Löwengeschwader'* He 111H-6 (1H+HN) departs its airfield in Norway bound for England during the Battle of Britain. The individual aircraft code letter H is RLM 23 Red (FS31140) outlined in White. This aircraft's tail swastika was overpainted in Black Green for an unknown reason. The Luftwaffe had 463 He 111s deployed in France, Belgium, and Norway when the Battle of Britain began on 13 August 1940. (Punka Archiv)

An He 111H-6 (G1+AN) assigned to 5/KG 55 *'Greifengeschwader'* is parked near Chartres Cathedral in France during the fall of 1940. The 'Griffin Wing' flew both He 111Ps and He 111Hs during the Battle of Britain. KG 55's insignia used the coat of arms of Giessen, the German city where the Wing was stationed before World War Two. (Löhr)

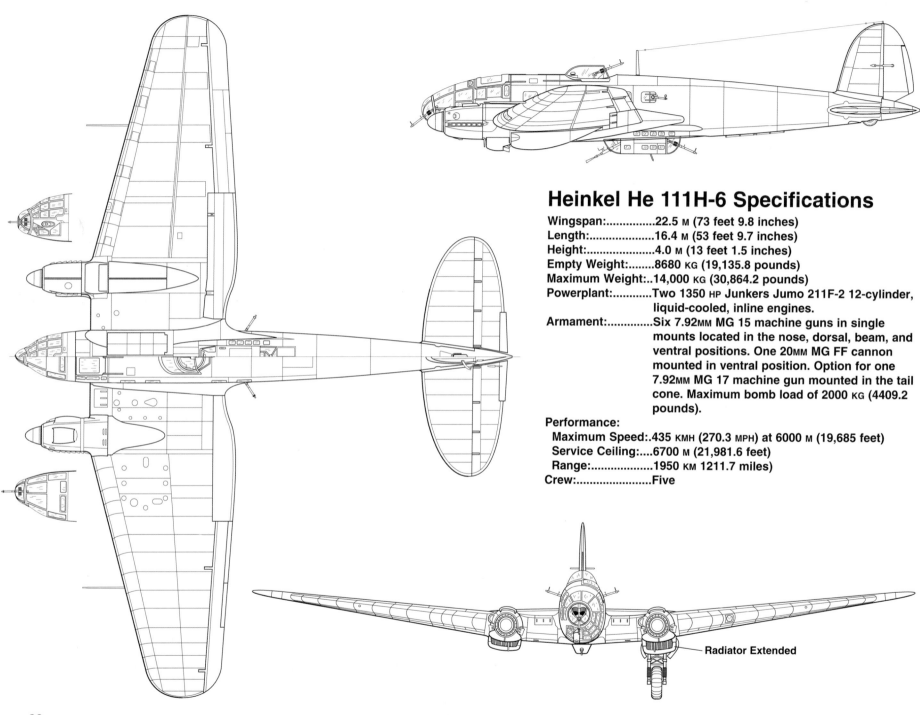

Heinkel He 111H-6 Specifications

Wingspan:...............22.5 m (73 feet 9.8 inches)
Length:....................16.4 m (53 feet 9.7 inches)
Height:....................4.0 m (13 feet 1.5 inches)
Empty Weight:........8680 KG (19,135.8 pounds)
Maximum Weight:..14,000 KG (30,864.2 pounds)
Powerplant:............Two 1350 HP Junkers Jumo 211F-2 12-cylinder, liquid-cooled, inline engines.
Armament:..............Six 7.92MM MG 15 machine guns in single mounts located in the nose, dorsal, beam, and ventral positions. One 20MM MG FF cannon mounted in ventral position. Option for one 7.92MM MG 17 machine gun mounted in the tail cone. Maximum bomb load of 2000 KG (4409.2 pounds).

Performance:
  Maximum Speed:.435 KMH (270.3 MPH) at 6000 M (19,685 feet)
  Service Ceiling:....6700 M (21,981.6 feet)
  Range:...................1950 KM 1211.7 miles)
Crew:.......................Five

Radiator Extended

A Junkers Jumo 211F engine is placed near an He 111H-6 under construction at a German factory. The Jumo 211F was a 12-cylinder, liquid-cooled, inverted inline engine. The large curved piping running along the aft end of the foreground engine is the supercharger duct. Early He 111H-6s received the 1300 HP Jumo 211F-1, while later aircraft were powered by the 1340 HP Jumo 211F-2.

Engines for He 111P/H Variants

Aircraft	Horsepower	Engine
He 111P-2/4	1100 HP	Daimler-Benz DB 601A-1
He 111P-6	1175 HP	DB 601N
He 111H-1	1010 HP	Junkers Jumo 211A-1
He 111H-3/4	1200 HP	Jumo 211D-1 or
	1400 HP	Jumo 211F-1
He 111H-5/6	1300 HP	Jumo 211F-1
He 111H-16/21	1340 HP	Jumo 211F-2
He 111H-23	1775 HP	Jumo 213A-1

(Right) Two crewman stand atop an He 111H-6 being refueled at a Luftwaffe airbase. Fuel lines run to the aircraft's fuel tanks inside the mid-fuselage and inboard wing sections. This He 111H variant introduced individual exhaust stubs instead of the collective exhaust tubes used on earlier He 111Hs. The oil cooler air intake is mounted atop the nacelle, while the supercharger air intake is mounted on the starboard side. The engine radiator air intake is located on the lower nacelle.

A crewman performs maintenance on the starboard wing of an He 111H-6, which is parked on a snow-covered airfield in Norway. This variant introduced the wide chord Junkers VS-11 wooden propeller, which replaced the narrow chord VDM metal propeller of earlier He 111s. The VS 11's increased width allowed it to better grab thin air at high altitude, while the wood construction conserved scarce metals. (Bundesarchiv)

A fuel truck is parked in front of an He 111H-6 at an airfield in German-occupied Russia. The He 111H-6 retained the same main landing gear and tail wheel configurations of previous He 111 variants, although main gear tire sizes increased to accommodate greater aircraft weights. (Bundesarchiv)

An He 111H-6 warms up its engines prior to a night mission. The single main gear tires are mounted onto a main strut, with a retraction strut running from just above the wheel axle to the gear bay. He 111 main landing gears fully retracted, while tailwheels on He 111P and H variants partially retracted. (Smithsonian Institution)

Early He 111s were equipped with VDM three bladed metal propellers. These propellers featured narrow blades and had variable pitch for various flight conditions. The VDM propeller was replaced by Junkers VS-11 wooden propellers on the He 111H-6. (Smithsonian Institution)

This He 111H-6 (NG+JQ) was assigned to Field Marshal Albert Kesselring as his personal transport during 1942. Kesselring commanded Luftwaffe operations in the Mediterranean, then commanded Axis forces in Italy. Upper surfaces are RLM 02 Gray (FS36165), with RLM 65 Light Blue (FS35352) undersurfaces. The propeller spinners are RLM 23 Red (leading) and white. (Löhr)

A pilot stands in his raised seat of an He 111H-6 assigned to I/KG 27 'Boelcke.' The small windshield is deployed for taxiing, take off, and landing, while the pilot has his head raised over the fuselage. His canopy slid aft for this procedure and for emergency escape. The I/KG 27 insignia – a stork carrying a bomb – is painted aft of the nose glazing. (Punka Archiv)

A Royal Hungarian Air Force air crewman stands beside his He 111H-6 in the western Soviet Union in late 1943. Canvas covers were placed over the engine nacelles of this aircraft, which has a 20MM MG FF cannon in the nose. Hungary flew German-supplied He 111s on reconnaissance missions over the Eastern Front from 1942 until early 1943. (Punka Archiv)

39

An He 111H bombardier/navigator practices aiming a 20mm MG FF cannon in the nose of his aircraft. The weapon was highly effective against trains and other surface targets when the bomber flew at low level. The MG FF was sighted using the L-FF/6 sight. This He 111H is also equipped with a *Kuto-Nase* (Nose Cutter) balloon cable cutter along the port side. (Schmidt)

The nose-mounted MG FF is fitted with a conical muzzle flash suppressor, which reduced the blinding muzzle flash in the bombardier/navigator's and pilot's eyes at night. This He 111H was field modified with two 13mm Rheinmetall MG 131 machine guns below the nose cone for additional frontal firepower. The bomber operated in the Orscha and Smolensk areas of the Soviet Union in late 1942. (Schmidt)

13mm MG 131 Machine Gun

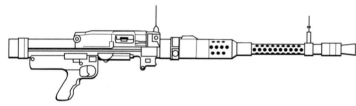

Length:................116.8 cm (46 inches)
Weight:................18.1 kg (40 pounds)
Muzzle Velocity:.722.4 m (2370 feet) per second
Rate of Fire:........900 rounds per minute

(Left) An 8/KG 53 He 111H-6 (A1+NS) comes in for a landing following a mission over the Eastern Front. This bomber is armed with a 20mm MG FF and a 7.92mm MG 15 in the nose. A PVC 1006L external bomb rack is mounted to the port fuselage undersurface. The fully lowered flaps allowed the He 111H-6 to land at 135 kmh (83.9 mph). This aircraft's code letter N is red outlined in white, while the rest of the code is black. RLM 27 Yellow undersurface wingtips and aft fuselage band indicated assignment to the Eastern Front. (Punka Archiv)

This He 111H-6 assigned to KG 26 is armed with two 765 ᴋɢ (1686.5 pound) LT F5b torpedoes. The weapons were mounted on PVC 1006 racks fitted to the fuselage undersurface. Temporary wooden fins stabilized the torpedo's entry into the water, then broke away from the weapon. The torpedo was believed to have a dark gray nose and an aluminum body. In early 1941, KG 26 deployed from Norway to Grosetto, Italy for anti-shipping operations in the Mediterranean Sea theatre. (Punka Archiv)

A forward-firing 20ᴍᴍ MG FF cannon is mounted in the ventral gondola of this He 111H-10 (A1+LL) of 3/KG 53 'Legion Condor.' This weapon was primarily used to attack surface targets on land and sea, although it was also employed against enemy aircraft. He 111 gunners nicknamed the gondola the 'Sterbebett' ('Deathbed'), due to their vulnerability to enemy fire. The aircraft's undersurfaces are overpainted black for night bombing missions. (Punka Archiv)

Dorsal Armament Development

Ventral Armament Development

He 111H-6/10

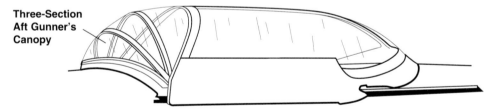

Three-Section Aft Gunner's Canopy

He 111H-6 (Port Side)

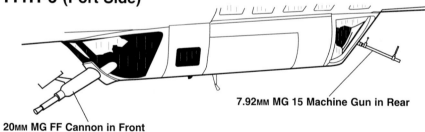

7.92ᴍᴍ MG 15 Machine Gun in Rear

20ᴍᴍ MG FF Cannon in Front

He 111H-10/18

Fixed Aft Gunner's Canopy

He 111H-10/11 (Starboard Side)

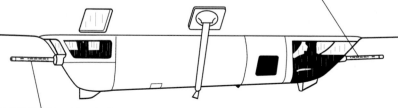

13ᴍᴍ MG 131 Machine Gun in Front

7.92ᴍᴍ MG 81Z Machine Gun in Rear

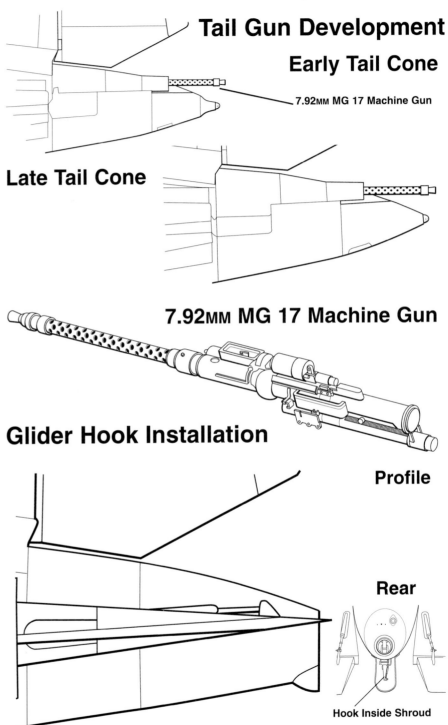

Tail Gun Development

Early Tail Cone

7.92MM MG 17 Machine Gun

Late Tail Cone

7.92MM MG 17 Machine Gun

Glider Hook Installation

Profile

Rear

Hook Inside Shroud

A Luftwaffe armorer services the 7.92MM Rheinmetall MG 17 machine gun fitted to the tail-cone of this He 111H-6 (*Werk Nr.* 7890). Some He 111Hs were equipped with this weapon, which the dorsal gunner fired by remote control. The MG 17 was fixed in place; the pilot had to maneuver the aircraft to aim the gun at pursuing enemy fighters. This weapon had a firing rate of 1100 rounds per minute, the same as for the earlier MG 15. (Löhr)

Ground crewmen prepare a DFS 230 glider for towing by an He 111H-6 (F7+BS) on the Eastern Front in late 1942. The bomber was assigned to *Schleppgruppe* (Towing Group) 1, which towed DFS 230s and other gliders on resupply missions over the front. A rigid towing hook mounted inside the He 111H-6's tailcone towed the glider immediately behind the bomber. (Jules Bernard)

He 111H-8 Cable Cutter Installation

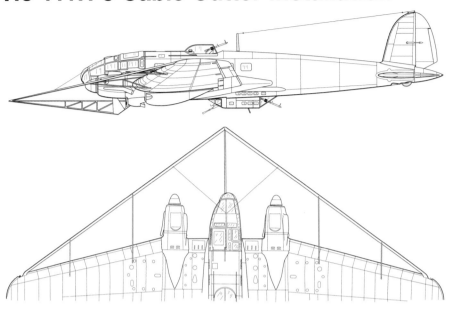

Alternate Cable Cutter Installation

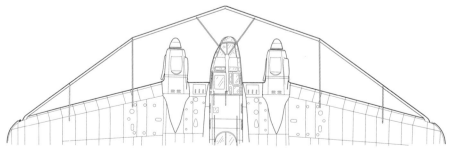

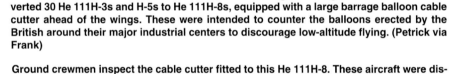

An He 111H-8 flies lead with a standard He 111H during a training mission. Heinkel converted 30 He 111H-3s and H-5s to He 111H-8s, equipped with a large barrage balloon cable cutter ahead of the wings. These were intended to counter the balloons erected by the British around their major industrial centers to discourage low-altitude flying. (Petrick via Frank)

Ground crewmen inspect the cable cutter fitted to this He 111H-8. These aircraft were distributed among the *Kampfgeschwadern* (Bomber Wings) deployed against Britain and flew in advance of the main force to sever the barrage balloon cables. The added weight of the cutter and its tail-mounted counterweight made the He 111H-8 difficult to fly, which shortened its service career. (Petrick)

An He 111H-10 equipped with *Kuto-Nase* (Nose Cutter) cable cutters rests on an airfield after its port landing gear collapsed. This incident occurred in German-occupied Russia in 1942. The *Kuto-Nase* run along the nose contours, above the nose-mounted machine gun. Wingtip-mounted *Kuto* (Cutter) devices (unseen in this photograph) complemented the *Kuto-Nase*. These cutters replaced the larger and heavier cutter mounted on He 111H-8s.

Maintenance crews service an He 111H-11 (A1+BH) assigned to 1/KG 53 *'Legion Condor'* in France. A 7.92ᴍᴍ Mauser MG 81Z twin-barrel machine gun is mounted in the port beam position; another such weapon was fitted to the starboard beam. The MG 81Z's rate of fire was 1200 to 1500 rounds per minute and it was often mounted in later He 111Hs for increased firepower. Some aircraft carried the MG 81I single-barrel version in the beam and gondola positions. (War's End via Petrick)

He 111H-10 Cable Cutters

Kuto-Nase on Nose

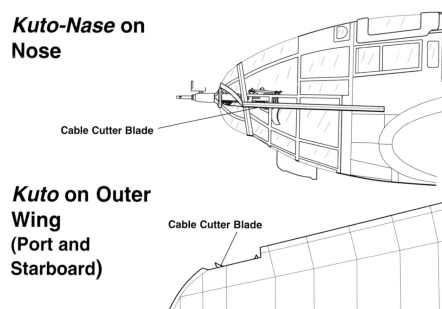

Cable Cutter Blade

Kuto on Outer Wing (Port and Starboard)

Cable Cutter Blade

7.92ᴍᴍ MG 81 Machine Guns

MG 81I Single-Barrel Machine Gun

MG 81Z Twin-Barrel Machine Gun

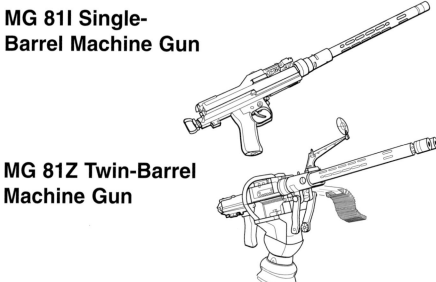

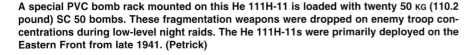
A special PVC bomb rack mounted on this He 111H-11 is loaded with twenty 50 KG (110.2 pound) SC 50 bombs. These fragmentation weapons were dropped on enemy troop concentrations during low-level night raids. The He 111H-11s were primarily deployed on the Eastern Front from late 1941. (Petrick)

This He 111H-11 parked on a Hungarian airfield has a white *Spiralschnauze* (Spiral Snout) painted on the starboard propeller spinner. This marking was unusual for Luftwaffe bombers, although it was common for fighters during this period. The He 111H-10 parked in the background is armed with a 20MM MG FF cannon with flash hider in the nose for night bombing missions. The He 111H-11 is also equipped with this weapon, but without the flash hider. (Punka Archiv)

He 111H-11

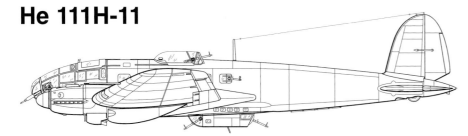

The crew of this He 111H-11 gather in front of their aircraft following a 'wheels up' landing near a Hungarian village in early 1944. This landing was chosen due to either battle damage or mechanical problems preventing main landing gear extension. This He 111 was fitted with the *Kuto-Nase* balloon cable cutter on the nose. (Punka Archiv)

He 111H-14

Added Antennas for Pathfinding Radio Equipment

He 111H-16 through H-23

The third large-scale He 111H production standard– following the He 111H-3 and He 111H-6 – was the **He 111H-16**, which entered production in late 1942. This new variant was developed from the He 111H-14 for the night bomber role and had a similar defensive armament to the He 111H-11.

The He 111H-16 had a wingspan of 22.5 M (73 feet 9.8 inches), a length of 16.4 M (53 feet 9.7 inches), and a height of 4 M (13 feet 1.5 inches). The aircraft weighed 6900 KG (15,211.6 pounds) empty and 14,000 KG (30,864.2 pounds) fully loaded for take off. The He 111H-16 was powered by two 1340 HP Junkers Jumo 211F-2 12-cylinder, liquid-cooled, inline engines. These enabled this variant to reach a maximum speed of 434 KMH (269.7 MPH) at 6000 M (19,685 feet). The aircraft's cruising speed was 390 KMH (242.3 MPH), while its service ceiling was 8500 M (27,887.1 feet). The He 111H-16 had a range of 2000 KM (1242.8 miles) when fully loaded.

The FuG 10P, FuG 16, FuBl Z, and APZ 6 radios were fitted to this variant for communications and navigation at night, while some aircraft received the FuG 101a radar altimeter. *Kuto-Nase* and *Kuto* cable cutters were sometimes mounted on the He 111H-16's nose and wing leading edges.

Defensive armament included single 13MM Rheinmetall MG 131 machine guns in the nose (*A-Stand*) and dorsal (B-Stand) positions. Some aircraft replaced the dorsal position with a DL131 electrically-powered turret armed with one MG 131 and were designated as **He 111H-16/R1**s. The beam and aft ventral positions each received 7.92MM Mauser MG 81Z

An He 111H-16/R2 (PK+GR) flies with two other He 111s – including the camera ship – over the Eastern Front in early 1943. An E – believed to be painted white – is on the near aircraft's rudder, but its exact purpose is unknown. This variant was equipped with a tail-mounted glider towing equipment, in addition to its primary bombing role. (Bundesarchiv)

twin-barrel machine guns. The 20MM Rheinmetall MG FF cannon was deleted, since the He 111H-16s were seldom employed on low-level missions.

The He 111H-16 retained its eight ESAC internal bomb cells, although the four port cells could be replaced by a 835 L (220.6 gallon) fuel tank like on previous variants. ETC 2000 racks could be installed over the bomb cell openings for external weapons carriage. Offensive armament combinations included eight 250 KG (551.1 pound) SC 250 or thirty-two 50 kg (110.2 pound) SC 50 bombs on external racks, or four SC 250s carried internally and one 1000 KG (2204.6 pound) SC 1000 bomb carried externally. The 2000 KG (4409.2 pound) maximum bomb load was increased to 3000 KG (6613.8 pounds) when He 111H-16s were fitted with two *R-Gerät*[1] Rocket Assisted Take Off (RATO) units under the wings. He 111H-16s seldom employed the *R-Gerät* in service.

In addition to the He 111H-16/R1, there were two additional sub-variants. The **He 111H-16/R2** was equipped with a boom-type coupling for glider towing, while the **He 111H-16/R3** was a dedicated pathfinder aircraft. The latter sub-variant had additional armor protection for its crew and a reduced bomb load.

German factories built 1155 He 111H-16s between the end of 1942 and the end of 1943. Additionally, 280 He 111H-6s and 35 He 111H-11s were updated to H-16 standard during this same period.

The proposed **He 111H-17** dual-control trainer – based on the He 111H-6 and H-11 – was cancelled before production. The **He 111H-18** was a long-range night bomber similar to the He 111H-16/R3. A 20MM MG FF cannon was fitted in the nose, while a 13MM MG 131 machine gun was mounted in the dorsal position and a 7.92MM MG 81Z twin-barrel weapon fitted to the ventral gondola. Beam machine guns were deleted and the crew reduced to three men (pilot, radio operator/dorsal gunner, and ventral gunner) for weight reduction purposes. The He 111H-18 carried a 2000 KG (4409.2 pound) bomb load to a range of 2800 KM (1739.9 miles). It was powered by two 1340 HP Jumo 211F-2 engines.

The **He 111H-18/R1** had additional armor protection for its crew, while the **He 111H-18/R2** replaced the dorsal gun position with a DL 131 electrically operated turret with one 13MM MG

[1]*R-Gerät*: *Rauchgerät*, Smoke Equipment; i.e., Auxiliary take off assistance device.

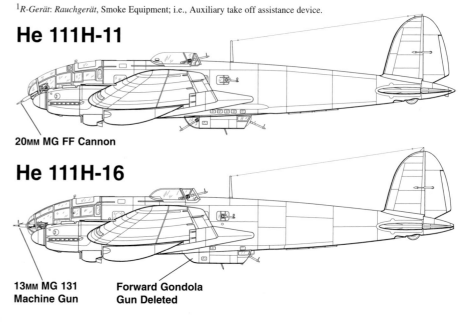

He 111H-11

20MM MG FF Cannon

He 111H-16

13MM MG 131 Machine Gun

Forward Gondola Gun Deleted

131. The **He 111H-18/R3** had flame dampers mounted over the exhausts of the 1340 HP Jumo 211F-2 engines for night operations. Heinkel built only 30 He 111H-18s in 1943 and these aircraft served with units in France and on the Russian Front. The **He 111H-19** was intended as a dual-control trainer based on the He 111H-16. The 13MM dorsal gun was retained, but all other armament was removed. This variant was cancelled in early 1944.

The last major He 111H series was the **He 111H-20**, which entered production in early 1944. It was proceeded by the **He 111 V46** and **He 111 V48** prototypes and were based on the He 111H-16 airframe. This new variant was intended to perform in several roles, including those of bomber, transport, and glider tug. Four He 111H-20 sub-variants were built, beginning with the **He 111H-20/R1** paratroop transport. This aircraft had a crew of three (pilot, navigator, and radio operator/dorsal gunner) and carried up to 16 paratroops. These troops exited the aircraft through a hatch located at the rear of the ventral gondola. Two 800 KG (1763.7 pound) supply containers were loaded onto ETC 1000 bomb racks under the fuselage for parachute dropping to ground troops. The He 111H-20 had a wingspan of 22.5 M (73 feet 9.8 inches), with a length of 16.4 M (53 feet 9.7 inches) and a height of 4 M (13 feet 1.5 inches).

The **He 111H-20/R2** was a freighter and glider tug, also crewed by three men. This sub-variant replaced the obsolete Junkers Ju 52/3m transport in those roles. The **He 111H-20/R3** night medium bomber added beam and ventral gunners to the crew. It carried a 2000 KG (4409.2 pound) external bomb load. The **He 111H-20/R4** nocturnal harassment bomber was armed with twenty 50 KG (110.2 pound) bombs and saw action on the Eastern Front.

All He 111H-20 bombers were armed with single 13MM MG 131 machine guns in the nose, ventral, and dorsal positions. The latter weapon was fitted inside a DL131 electrically operated turret. One 7.92MM Mauser MG 81Z twin-barrel machine gun was mounted in both the port and starboard beam positions. Radio equipment fitted in this variant included the FuG 10P, FuG 16, APZ 6, FuBl Z, FuG 101A, and FuG 25A sets.

The He 111H-20 was powered by two 1750 HP Junkers Jumo 213E-1 12-cylinder, liquid-cooled, inline engines. These engines turned three-bladed Junkers VS 11 wooden variable pitch propellers. Exhaust flame dampers were normally fitted on all He 111H-20s. This variant had a maximum take off weight of 14,500 KG (31,966.5 pounds). It had a maximum speed

Engine Nacelle Development

He 111H-10 through H-16

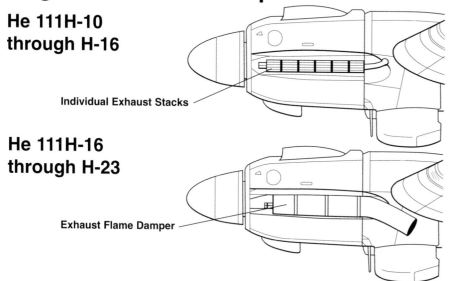

Individual Exhaust Stacks

He 111H-16 through H-23

Exhaust Flame Damper

Ground crewmen prepare an He 111H-16 (NI+JE) for a mission over snow-covered Russia in early 1943. The aircraft is assigned to *Schleppgruppe* (Towing Group) 4, although it had a secondary bombing function. The He 111H-16 is armed with a 7.92MM MG 81Z twin-barrel machine gun in the dorsal position. (Löhr)

The same He 111H-16 (NI+JE) warms up its Jumo 211F-2 inline engines prior to a mission over the Eastern Front. The aircraft has a temporary white finish over the standard RLM 70 Black Green and RLM 71 Dark Green camouflage. The *Schleppgruppe* 4 insignia is painted on the nose, under the pilot's window. The nose-mounted 20MM MG FF cannon was used against both enemy aircraft and surface targets. (Löhr)

An He 111H-16/R1 (+AH) lies damaged at Hradec Králové airfield, Czechoslovakia in May of 1945. Retreating German troops damaged the aircraft to prevent its use by advancing Soviet forces. This variant featured a turret-mounted 13MM MG 131 machine gun in the dorsal position. RLM 76 Light Gray (FS36473) mottling was painted over the upper surface camouflage. (Zdenek)

The He 111H-18 was equipped with the FuG 200 'Lichtenstein' radar antenna on its nose. This radar was used to guide the bomber on surface attacks at night and bad weather. This variant retained the nose-mounted 20MM MG FF cannon. The few He 111H-18s built saw action on both the Western and Eastern fronts in 1944.

of 350 KMH (217.5 MPH) at 8300 M (27,231 feet). Heinkel and its licensees built 550 He 111H-20s through the summer of 1944, while 586 He 111H-6s were upgraded to H-20 standard during the same period.

Heinkel built 22 **He 111H-21**s in the late spring and summer of 1944. This mated 1350 HP Jumo 211F-2 engines to the He 111H-20 airframe. The combination resulted in an He 111 with superior high altitude performance. It had a top speed of 480 KMH (298.3 MPH) at 7000 M (22,965.9 feet) and a service ceiling of 10,000 M (32,808.4 feet). Priority on Jumo 211F-2 deliveries for the Focke-Wulf Fw 190D fighter ended the He 111H-21 production run.

The **He 111H-22** was a variant used to carry one Fieseler Fi 103A-1 flying bomb, also called the V-1[2] 'buzz bomb.' An He 111H successfully tested this concept at the German rocket test center at Peenemünde during the winter of 1943-44. Several He 111H-16s and H-20s were converted to carry a V-1 under either the port or starboard wing between the fuselage and the engine nacelle. An ETC 2000 rack was modified to hold the flying bomb in place before launch. Steel plating was placed on the forward section of the horizontal stabilizer aft of the missile. This plating shielded the stabilizer from the hot exhaust of the V-1's pulse jet engine.

Most He 111H-22s were delivered to II *Gruppe* (Group), KG (*Kampfgeschwader*; Bomber Wing) 53 from 7 July 1944. This unit was based in northwest Germany and Holland to fly night missions against targets in Great Britain. The bombers approached their targets from 90 M (295.3 feet) above the North Sea while flying at 275 KMH (170.9 MPH). The He 111H-22s then climbed to 400 M (1312.3 feet) and accelerated to 320 KMH (198.8 MPH) when they were 100 to 150 KM (62.1 to 93.2 miles) from the target. The V-1's engine was then started and warmed up for ten seconds before it was released by the He 111H-22 and sent to its target. The V-1 exhaust flame gave away the intruder's location to British night fighters, who downed most of the approximately 80 He 111H-22s lost in action. Several other bombers were destroyed in accidents.

[2]V: *Vergeltungswaffe*; Vengeance Weapon

He 111H-16

He 111H-18

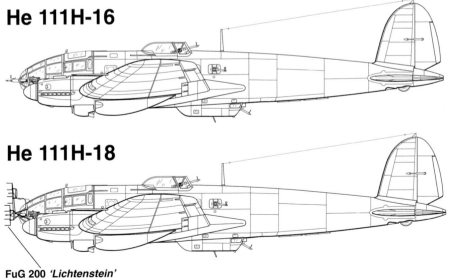

FuG 200 'Lichtenstein'
Radar Antenna

The final He 111H series variant was the **He 111H-23** long-range transport. Twelve He 111H-20s on the production line were converted to this variant during the fall of 1944. Armament was reduced to single 13MM MG 131 machine guns in the nose and the dorsal turret, plus one 7.92MM MG 81Z weapon in the ventral gondola. The cabin accommodated eight paratroopers, who exited the aircraft through a ventral hatch similar to the one in the He 111H-20/R1. Two external racks under the fuselage held 800 KG supply containers that were air dropped for the paratroopers' use. The He 111H-23s were intended for use by KG 200, the Luftwaffe's special operations wing; however, the unit had aircraft already in place for dropping agents by parachute. Forward maintenance units converted the 12 He 111H-23s built into night bombers.

It is estimated that 7585 He 111s of all types were built between 1935 and 1944, including 6615 He 111P and He 111H aircraft. After World War Two ended, Spain's *Construcciones Aeronáuticas SA* (CASA) built 130 He 111H-16s under a license granted in 1944. The Spanish-built aircraft were designated **CASA 2111**s and were used in bombing, reconnaissance, and transport roles. Shortages of Jumo 211F-2 engines resulted in the last 70 CASA 2111s being fitted with 1600 HP Rolls-Royce Merlin 500-20 and 500-29 inline engines. This was completed between 1953 and 1956 and the CASA 2111 remained in Spanish Air Force service until the early 1970s.

A KG 55 He 111H-20 prepares to taxi out on a night raid on London in early 1944. The bombardier/navigator leans out his open window to get final instructions from the ground crew. This bomber has exhaust flame dampers, a refined *Kuto-Nase*, and is armed with a 1000 KG (2204.6 pound) PC 1000RS bomb under the port fuselage. (Löhr)

Nose Armament Development

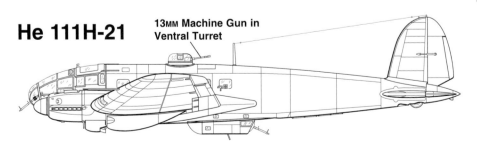

He 111H-16
13MM Machine Gun in Hooded Ventral Compartment

He 111H-16

20MM MG FF Cannon, with L-FF/6 Sight Mounted Atop Weapon

He 111H-21
13MM Machine Gun in Ventral Turret

He 111H-20 through H-23

13MM MG131 Machine Gun

Spent Cartridge Port

The He 111H-20's defensive armament included a 13MM MG 131 machine gun in a DL131 dorsal turret. This electrically-powered turret traversed 360° for improved protection against enemy fighters. A circular EZ-6 radio direction finder antenna is mounted to the upper fuselage forward of the turret. Flame dampers were fitted to the engine exhausts for night bombing missions. (Petrick)

The He 111H-20's defensive armament included 7.92MM MG 81Z twin-barrel machine guns in the port and starboard beam positions. The weapons were fitted inside covered windows, which allowed the gunner to fire without exposure to the airstream. The radio antenna base is mounted aft of the 13MM machine gun turret. (Petrick)

Dorsal Armament Development

He 111H-16

13MM MG 131
in Fixed
Canopy

He 111H-21

13MM MG 131 in DL 131 Turret

Ventral Armament Development

He 111H-11 (Starboard Side)

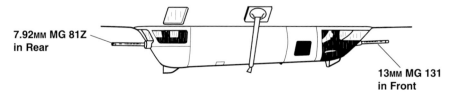

7.92MM MG 81Z
in Rear

13MM MG 131
in Front

He 111H-16 through H-23 (Port Side)

Front Weapon
Deleted

7.92MM MG
81Z in Rear

An He 111H-21 assigned to KG 4 *'General Wever'* is refueled at an airfield in Hungary in the late summer of 1944. The code letters aft of the fuselage *Balkenkreuz* are a red B and a black V. RLM 76 Light Gray lines are painted over the upper surfaces. A 13MM MG 131 machine gun is mounted in the aft gondola position. This weapon had a muzzle velocity of 2370 M (7775.6 feet) per second and a firing rate of 900 rounds per minute. (Punka Archiv)

He 111H-22 with Fi 103 (V1) under Starboard Wing

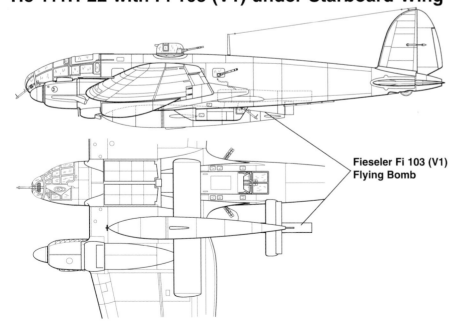

Fieseler Fi 103 (V1) Flying Bomb

A Fieseler Fi 103A-1 (V-1) flying bomb is mounted under the starboard wing of this He 111H-22 (5K+GA) of *Stab*/KG 3. This Wing flew from bases in Holland and Germany from late July of 1944, launching V-1s against London and Southampton, England. The flying bomb's pulse jet engine was started prior to its release from the He 111H-22.

The He 111H-20/R1 and later He 111H-23 were paratroop transport variants built in mid-to late 1944. An aft gondola section opening allowed 16 paratroops to egress from the aircraft. This He 111H-20/R1 (NT+SL, *Werk Nr.* 701152) is displayed at the Royal Air Force Museum in Hendon, England.

He 111R and He 111Z

By 1943, the Luftwaffe sought a bomber with a higher service ceiling than the He 111's 6000 M (19,685 feet) ceiling. Heinkel responded by proposing the **He 111R** high altitude bomber to the RLM. The **He 111R-1** was to be powered by two 1300 HP Junkers Jumo 211F-1 engines with turbo superchargers and annular (circular) radiators. The Luftwaffe felt this variant's estimated performance was insufficient to meet their requirements and Heinkel proposed the **He 111R-2** in early 1944.

This sub-variant's powerplant was to be the 1810 HP Daimler-Benz DB 603U, with either Hirth or TKL 15 turbo-superchargers. Annular radiators similar to those designed for the He 111R-1 were intended for the R-2. This aircraft's estimated maximum speed was 500 KMH (310.7 MPH) and its ceiling was to have been 14,000 M (45,931.8 feet). An He 111H-6 was modified to serve as the **He 111 V32** prototype for flight tests in early 1944. This aircraft had DB 603U engines and TK 9 AC turbo-superchargers. Unsatisfactory test results led to the He 111R's cancellation.

The most unusual He 111 variant ever produced was the **He 111Z** (*Zwilling*, Twin) transport and glider tug, which began development in early 1941. A suitable aircraft was required to tow the Messerschmitt Me 321 *Gigant* (Giant) heavy glider. No single Luftwaffe aircraft was powerful enough to tow this glider, which weighed 34,400 KG (75,837.7 pounds) fully loaded. Attempts by three Messerschmitt Bf 110 heavy fighters flying in unison to tow the Me 321 frequently met with disaster.

Heinkel took two He 111H-6s, removed one outer wing from each aircraft, and joined them with an outer wing center section housing a fifth 1350 HP Junkers Jumo 211F-2 engine. The resulting **He 111Z-1** had a wingspan of 35.4 M (116 feet 1.7 inches), while the length of 16.4 M (53 feet 9.7 inches) and height of 4 M (13 feet 1.5 inches) remained the same as for the standard He 111H-6. The new variant weighed 21,300 KG (46,957.7 pounds) empty and 29,600 KG (65,255.7 pounds) at take off.

The He 111Z-1 had a maximum speed of 437 KMH (271.5 MPH) at 6000 M (19,685 feet) and a cruising speed of 394 KMH (244.8 MPH). Its service ceiling was 10,200 M (33,464.6 feet) and its maximum range was 4000 KM (2485.6 miles). Four 900 L (237.8 gallon) external fuel tanks were optionally mounted under the two fuselages, increasing the aircraft's total fuel capacity to 4850 L (1281.2 gallons). The fuel load gave the He 111Z-1 a flight endurance of ten hours. It could tow one Me 321 heavy glider or two Gotha Go 242 medium gliders.

Either a 7.92MM MG 15 or a 13MM MG 131 machine gun was mounted in the port nose, while a 20MM MG FF cannon was fitted in the starboard nose. Single MG 131s were mounted in the two dorsal positions, while each ventral gondola had a single aft-firing MG 15. Single MG 15s were mounted in both outboard beam positions.

The pilot flew the He 111Z-1 from the port cockpit, while the assistant pilot/navigator sat in the starboard cockpit. Both cockpits had dual controls, but only the pilot had throttles for the five engines. Each pair of main landing gear was operated from its respective cockpit. The remainder of the seven-main crew consisted of a mechanic, radio operator, and gunner in the port fuselage and a mechanic and gunner to starboard.

Heinkel built two prototypes (the He 111Z V1 and V2), both of which successfully flew in the late fall of 1941. The flight test program at the *E-Stelle* (Test Center) in Rechlin was successfully completed in January of 1942. Production began soon afterward and towing trials were performed at Rechlin in May of 1942. The arrival of the Me 323 – the six-engined version of the Me 321 glider – ended the He 111Z-1 production run at ten aircraft in the late spring of 1942.

The He 111Z-1 first saw action on 11 February 1943, when aircraft assigned to I *Gruppe* of LLG 2 (*Luftlandegeschwader*; Air Landing Wing) each towed two Gotha Go 242 medium gliders. These missions were undertaken to resupply German forces fighting the Soviets in the Kuban region of southwest Russia. Enemy action and unsuitable airfields destroyed three He 111Z-1s and damaged several more during this campaign. Five more aircraft were lost by September of 1944, then the unit was disbanded.

In 1944, the RLM (Reich Air Ministry) proposed developing long range bomber and reconnaissance versions of the He 111Z, designated **He 111Z-2** and **He 111Z-3**, respectively. The He 111Z-2 bomber was to carry a 7000 KG (15,432.1 pound) bomb load 4000 KM (2485.5 miles), while the He 111Z-3 reconnaissance aircraft had a 6000 KM (3728.3 mile) range. Neither variant was built, due to the development of Heinkel's He 177 *Greif* (Griffin) heavy bomber.

An He 111Z-1 is parked at Poltava airfield in the Ukraine in 1943. This variant combined two He 111H-6 fuselages with a new center wing section, which housed a fifth engine. Four 900 L (237.8 gallon) fuel tanks are carried under the fuselage sections. He 111Z-1s towed Messerschmitt Me 321 and Gotha Go 242 gliders on resupply missions from February of 1943. (Bagossy)

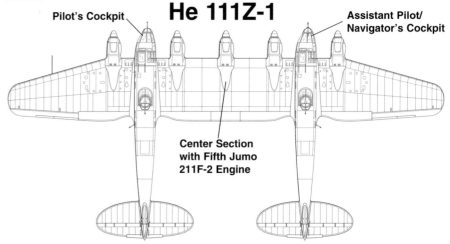

He 111Z-1

Pilot's Cockpit

Assistant Pilot/ Navigator's Cockpit

Center Section with Fifth Jumo 211F-2 Engine

He 111 in Service

The Heinkel He 111 first saw combat during the Spanish Civil War of 1936 to 1939. Germany deployed four He 111B-0s to Nationalist controlled territory, from where they flew their first combat mission against Republican-held Madrid on 9 March 1937. The He 111s were assigned to *Kampfgruppe* (Bomber Group) 88 of the *Legion Condor*, the German ground and air forces unit supporting General Francisco Franco's Nationalists. The He 111B-0s were joined by 40 He 111B-1 and 25 B-2 aircraft from May of 1937. The Germans instructed Spanish Nationalist crews to fly the He 111B, these bombers being transferred to Spanish control in early 1938. By this time, the *Legion Condor* was flying 45 He 111E-1s against Republican forces. German and Nationalist He 111s saw extensive service throughout the conflict, which ended in victory for Franco's Nationalists in March of 1939. The *Legion Condor* turned over its remaining He 111E-1s to the Spanish before returning to Germany that year.

The Luftwaffe had 808 He 111s in service when the *Wehrmacht* (German Armed Forces) invaded Poland on 1 September 1939. This total included 749 He 111P and H aircraft assigned to 21 *Gruppen* (Groups) and one *Staffel* (Squadron). The remaining 59 He 111s were of older E, F, and J versions. The bombers attacked Polish airfields from the onset of the war, destroying many Polish Air Force aircraft on the ground and knocking out runways, fuel and ammunition depots, and repair facilities. The Germans achieved air superiority in the first week of the war and the He 111s were redirected to attack Polish supply lines and cities. He 111s comprised most of the Luftwaffe bombers that attacked Warsaw and other Polish cities. Poland surrendered to German forces on 6 October 1939, ending the He 111's action over Eastern Europe for the time being.

Three He 111 bomber wings and a reconnaissance group led the German air assault against Norway on 9 April 1940. The bombers attacked Norwegian defenses and the hastily deployed British and French forces sent to Norway. Reconnaissance aircraft spotted Allied ships and directed German aircraft and ships to their attacks. Despite some losses to Allied fighters and anti-aircraft fire, the He 111s supplied the bulk of the Luftwaffe's bombing needs in the Norwegian campaign, which ended in German triumph on 10 June.

By this date, German forces were nearly completing their assault on the Low Countries (Belgium, the Netherlands, Luxembourg) and France. Prior to this invasion, He 111s flew reconnaissance and leaflet dropping missions over France during the 'Phony War'[1] of late 1939 and early 1940. The Luftwaffe had 641 He 111s in western Germany to support the invasion of Western Europe when it began on 10 May 1940. The He 111 bombers first attacked enemy airfields, then troop concentrations and lines of communication in support of German ground forces. KG 4's Heinkels attacked Rotterdam on 14 May, killing 850 civilians in what the Allies called a 'terror bombing.' After driving though the Low Countries, the Germans forced British and French troops to Dunkirk, France, from where many of them were evacuated to England. The *Wehrmacht* continued to drive into France, with He 111s providing much of the bomber support. France's armistice with Germany took effect on 26 June 1940.

Many He 111 units redeployed to airfields in northern France, Belgium, and the Netherlands as the French campaign ended. On 13 August 1940 – *Adlertag* (Eagle Day) – the Luftwaffe had 463 He 111s (124 He 111Ps and 339 He 111Hs) available to attack Great Britain. The He 111's vulnerabilities – low speed and light defensive armament – soon became apparent in the skies over England and the English Channel. It was unable to outrun the Hawker Hurricane

[1]The 'Phony War' described the inactivity on the Western Front between Allied (British and French) and German forces from 3 September 1939 until 10 May 1940.

Five He 111Ps fly in echelon formation off the camera aircraft's starboard wing in early 1939. Another He 111P flies well away from this group. The bombers are painted in the pre-war RLM 61/62/63 upper surface camouflage scheme, with five-digit fuselage codes. The unit insignia under the pilot's window is believed to belong to III/KG 255, which was redesignated III/KG 51 on 1 May 1939.

Several He 111P or H bombers assemble in formation for a daylight raid on England in late 1940. The undersurfaces and part of the fuselage sides were painted black for camouflage during night raids. White individual letters are painted to starboard of the fuselage *Balkenkreuz*. He 111s were largely confined to night missions over England from mid-September of 1940, after British fighters inflicted heavy losses on daylight raids. (Punka Archiv)

An He 111 flies over the English countryside on a daylight mission during the Battle of Britain. Low level clouds partly obscure the landscape from the air. The He 111's individual letter M was painted outboard of the upper wing crosses; however, the letter's color is unknown. (Punka Archiv)

A I/KG 6 He 111P or H flies over a French beach during the fall of 1940. The *Gruppe* insignia is painted on the nose, under the navigator/bombardier's window. Propeller spinners were painted in I *Gruppe's* color of white, while the black code 3E is painted to port of the fuselage national insignia. (Punka Archiv)

and Supermarine Spitfire fighters of the Royal Air Force (RAF), which were each armed with eight .303 caliber (7.7MM) machine guns. The He 111 units lost 60 aircraft in August of 1940. In September, the Luftwaffe switched from daylight to night raids. These missions reduced the vulnerability of the He 111s and other bombers – Dornier Do 17s and Junkers Ju 88s – to British air defenses, although bombing accuracy suffered. Several He 111s were equipped with radio target guidance systems and employed as pathfinders for the attack force. The *'X-Geräte'* using two intersecting radio beams was originally used. This was later replaced by the *'Y-Geräte'* locator system, which used only one guiding beam and was less vulnerable to British Electronic Countermeasures (ECM). Despite the cover of night, improving British night fighters and anti-aircraft fire took their toll of He 111s. The Luftwaffe lost 150 He 111s to enemy action during the first three months of 1941.

The Germans attacked London, Coventry, and other British cities during the 'Night Blitz,' which ran from September of 1940 until May of 1941. German operations in Eastern Europe resulted in the redeployment of many He 111s from Western European airfields. Those He 111s remaining in the West were transferred to anti-shipping and night harassment raids and reconnaissance missions. They were later replaced in service by newer Ju 88s and Dornier Do 217s.

While He 111s were attacking Britain at night, other He 111s were sent to the Mediterranean theatre. In December of 1940, 76 He 111s of three *Gruppen* were redeployed from Norway to Sicily. These bombers began attacking the British island of Malta in January of 1941. Several He 111s were modified as torpedo bombers and flew against Allied shipping in the Mediterranean. The Malta and anti-shipping missions continued well into 1942. The He 111s achieved some successes, but also took heavy losses as the campaign continued. Several He 111s were deployed to North Africa from late 1941, but saw mostly sporadic action in night bombing and resupply roles.

One He 111 *Gruppe* (Group) supported Germany's invasion of Yugoslavia and Greece, which began on 6 April 1941. The bombers attacked airfields, troop concentrations, and lines of communication. The campaign ended with a Germany victory in May, followed by a much larger campaign – the invasion of the Soviet Union.

The Luftwaffe had 212 He 111Hs and two He 111Ps in 13 bomber *Gruppen* when Operation BARBAROSSA – the German invasion – began on 22 June 1941. Additionally, 11 He 111s were assigned to three weather reconnaissance squadrons deployed on the Eastern Front. Two more He 111-equipped *Geschwadern* (Wings) were soon redeployed from Western Europe to replace aircraft lost to Soviet action. He 111s constituted the bulk of the Luftwaffe bombers sent against Moscow and Leningrad[2] in a series of night and day raids that summer and fall.

While the Germans advanced deeper into the Soviet Union, their supply lines lengthened. The dismal condition of Russian roads reduced shipments of fuel, bombs, and spare parts for the He 111s and other Luftwaffe aircraft. The poor state of captured Soviet airfields resulted in frequent He 111 undercarriage failures and reduced bomb and fuel loads. The Luftwaffe was hard-pressed to meet the ground forces' requirements for air support as this campaign continued.

In early 1942, He 111s primarily flew resupply missions to encircled German forces. That summer, the Heinkels of *Kampfgruppe* (Bomber Group) 100 successfully attacked Soviet fortifications at Sevastopol, using 1700 KG (3747.8 pound) SC 1700 and 2500 KG (5511.5 pound) SC 2500 bombs. The encirclement of the German Sixth Army at Stalingrad[3] in November of 1942 resulted in a massive German aerial resupply effort. The Luftwaffe's 300 He 111s in this

[2]Now St. Petersburg, Russia
[3]Now Volgograd, Russia

sector attacked Soviet forces while flying into the Stalingrad pocket, where they evacuated wounded troops. The German resupply effort was hampered by worsening weather, the distance from their airfields to Stalingrad, and by improved Soviet fighter and anti-aircraft defenses. Losses increased as the Soviets tightened the ring around the Sixth Army. After the last German-held airfield in Stalingrad was captured on 22 January 1943, the He 111s and other aircraft had to para-drop supplies to German forces. By Stalingrad's surrender on 2 February, the Luftwaffe lost 490 aircraft in the airlift effort, including 165 He 111s.

He 111s remained in the forefront of Luftwaffe combat on the Eastern Front throughout 1943. The bombers attacked troop concentrations and any Soviet factories that remained in reach. (The Soviets evacuated hundreds of arms factories to the east – out of German bomber range – in late 1941 and early 1942.) The greater number and improved effectiveness of Soviet fighters and anti-aircraft fire took a heavy toll on the He 111s, many of which were downed during the Battle of Kursk in July. The surviving He 111s were withdrawn to Poland in late 1943 for rest and reequipment.

The near continuous German retreats from Soviet territory saw the He 111s primarily employed for transport and glider-towing missions. These aircraft began replacing obsolete Junkers Ju 52/3ms in the Luftwaffe's transport units. The Heinkels continued to fly bombing missions, mostly at night or where the Germans could maintain air superiority over the front. One notable bombing mission occurred on 22 June 1944, when He 111s led a successful attack on Poltava airfield in the Ukraine. The night raid destroyed over 40 US bombers, which flew to Poltava on a shuttle bombing mission from England.

Luftwaffe units in Eastern Europe had 440 He 111s (260 of which were serviceable) when Soviet forces invaded Hungary in the fall of 1944. These aircraft primarily saw action in the transport role for the remainder of World War Two. The Allied strategic bombing campaign wrecked Germany's oil supply and transportation system, which greatly reduced the fuel and spare parts available to the remaining He 111s. Some resupply and evacuation missions were flown into the besieged city of Budapest, Hungary from December of 1944 until February of 1945. This was repeated in early 1945, when Soviet forces encircled Breslau[4] in the German region of Silesia. The last nine He 111s in service were destroyed by their crews in Bavaria before surrendering to US forces on 8 May 1945 – V-E (Victory in Europe) Day.

[4]Now Wroclaw, Poland

An He 111P equipped for pathfinding missions rests under camouflage netting at a Luftwaffe base in France in late 1940. Two mast antennas for the *'X-Geräte'* radio navigation equipment are mounted on the upper fuselage, aft of the radio direction finding loop antenna. The *'X-Geräte'* used intersecting radio signals to guide bombers to their targets at night. (Bundesarchiv)

A 6/KG 51 *'Edelweißgeschwader'* He 111H-6 (9K+CP) pulls up after releasing two LT F5b torpedoes. The anti-ship weapons just entered the water and are bound for their target. The bomber retained its black undersurfaces from its earlier night bomber deployment against England. (Punka Archiv)

An He 111H-6 (G1+EH) accompanies another He 111 on a raid on England during the fall of 1940. This bomber was assigned to 5/KG 55 during the *'Englandblitz'* raids. The He 111H-6's undersurfaces and sides were overpainted black. The tail swastika was painted over and only the white trimmed red E on the fuselage code was left intact. (Löhr)

White temporary paint covers the upper surfaces of this He 111H-6 (T5+UH) based on a Russian airfield in late 1941 or early 1942. This bomber is assigned to 1/*Aufklärungsgruppe Ob.d.L.* (Reconnaissance Group of the Air Force Commander-in-Chief). This unit flew long-range reconnaissance of strategic Allied targets to gather information for Luftwaffe senior commanders. The dorsal and beam weapons were removed to lighten the He 111H-6. (Löhr)

An He 111H releases a 500 KG (1102.3 pound) SC 500 bomb from one of its underfuselage PVC bomb racks over Russia. Two additional SC 500s are mounted under the fuselage, but are soon dropped on their targets. Temporary white paint appears on portions of the upper wing surfaces. The dorsal gunner's canopy is fully closed. (Punka Archiv)

General Adolf Galland was assigned this He 111H-3 (SI+MK) while serving as commander of Luftwaffe fighters in late 1941. The aft fuselage band and the code letters are both in RLM 27 Yellow (FS33637), although the band is farther forward than usual. Galland's aircraft is taxiing over a snow-covered airfield in the occupied Soviet Union. (Schulz)

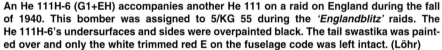

A delegation of Luftwaffe officers visits the airfield of the 1/1 Long Range Reconnaissance Squadron, Royal Hungarian Air Force. The Germans arrived in an He 111H configured as a courier aircraft, with internal bombing equipment removed. This visit was made to confer the Iron Cross 1st Class to several Hungarian airmen. (Punka Archiv)

Ground crewmen install a 700 KG (1543.2 pound) supply container under the fuselage of this KG 4 He 111H-6 on the Eastern Front in 1943. A second container awaits installation near the starboard wing. A parachute fitted to one end of this container slowed its descent after release from the aircraft. RLM 76 Light Gray mottling was painted over the He 111H-6's upper surfaces. (Schmidt)

A III/KG 26 He 111H (1H+DN) carries a 1000 KG (2204.6 pound) SC 1000 bomb on the port PVC underfuselage bomb rack. The gondola is armed with a 20MM MG FF at the front and a 7.92MM MG 15 aft. This Gruppe was deployed to Italy in 1941 for operations against Allied forces in the Mediterranean theater. Axis aircraft in this theater had white aft fuselage bands for identification. (Punka Archiv)

A KG 26 He 111H-6 begins its take off run on a snow-covered airfield in Russia. It is armed with a 1000 KG SC 1000 bomb on the port rack, which was the standard rack used when only one underfuselage external stores station was required. The He 111H-6 retains the black undersurfaces of its previous night bombing deployment over England. (Punka Archiv)

Wings of German Eagles
More Luftwaffe Aircraft from squadron/signal publications

1030 Bf 110 Zerstörer

1044 Bf 109, Part 1

1057 Bf 109, Part 2

1073 Ju 87 Stuka

1147 Me 210/410

1170 Fw 190

1176 Henschel Hs 129

5522 Fw 190A/F Walk Around

5524 Bf 110G Walk Around